Fiona Mapp

Success

GCSE Mathematics
Foundation
Workbook

Contents

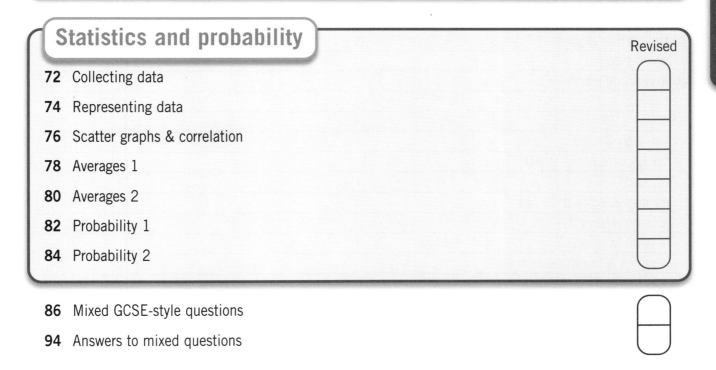

Geometry and measures

Revised

Statistics and probability

Revised

Contents

3

Homework diary

TOPIC	SCORE
Number revision	/27
Types of numbers	/41
Positive & negative numbers	/27
Working with numbers	/38
Fractions	/40
Decimals	/36
Percentages 1	/34
Percentages 2	/37
Fractions, decimals & percentages	/25
Approximations & using a calculator	/38
Ratio	/34
Indices	/51
Algebra	/36
Equations 1	/49
Equations 2 & inequalities	/29
Number patterns & sequences	/30
Formulae	/29
Straight-line graphs	/24
Curved graphs	/25
Interpreting graphs	/16
Shapes	/23
Solids	/20
Symmetry & constructions	/25
Loci & coordinates in 3D	/18
Angles	/34
Bearings & scale drawings	/22
Transformations 1	/22
Transformations 2	/18
Measures & measurement 1	/24
Measures & measurement 2	/39
Pythagoras' theorem	/31
Area of 2D shapes	/30
Volume of 3D shapes	/36
Collecting data	/20
Representing data	/25
Scatter graphs & correlation	/22
Averages 1	/31
Averages 2	/24
Probability 1	/29
Probability 2	/24

Revision & exam tips

Planning and revising:
- Mathematics should be revised **actively**. You should be doing **more than just reading**.
- Find out the dates of your first mathematics examination. Make an examination and revision timetable.
- After completing a topic in school, go through the topic again in the **GCSE Success Revision Guide**. Copy out the **main points, results** and **formulae** into a notebook or use a **highlighter** to emphasise them.
- Try to write out the **key points** from **memory**. Check what you have written and see if there are any differences.
- Revise in short bursts of about **30 minutes,** followed by a **short break**.
- Learn **facts** from your exercise books, notebooks and the **Success Revision Guide**. **Memorise** any formulae you need to learn.
- Learn with a friend to make it easier and more fun!
- Do the **multiple-choice** and **short-answer** questions in this book and check your answers to see how much you know.
- Once you feel **confident** that you know the topic, do the **GCSE-style** questions in this book. **Highlight** the key words in the question, **plan** your answer and then go back and **check** that you have answered the question.
- **Make a note** of any topics that you do not understand and **go back through** the notes again.

Different types of questions:
- On the **GCSE Mathematics papers** you will have several types of questions:
  Calculate – In these questions you need to work out the answer. Remember that it is important to show full working out.
  Explain – These questions want you to explain, with a mathematical reason or calculation, what the answer is.
  Show – These questions usually require you to show, with mathematical justification, what the answer is.
  Write down or state – These questions require no explanation or working out.
  Prove – These questions want you to set out a concise logical argument, making the reasons clear.
  Deduce – These questions make use of an earlier answer to establish a result.

On the day:
- **Follow the instructions** on the exam paper. Make sure that you understand what any **symbols** mean.
- Make sure that you **read the question** carefully so that you give the answer that an examiner wants.
- Always **show your working**; you may pick up some marks even if your final answer is wrong.
- Do **rough calculations** to check your answers and make sure that they are **reasonable.**
- When carrying out a calculation, **do not round the answer until the end**, otherwise your final answer will not be as accurate as is needed.
- Lay out your working **carefully** and **concisely**. Write down the calculations that you are going to make. You usually get marks for showing a **correct method**.
- Make your drawings and graphs **neat** and **accurate**.
- Know what is on the **formulae page** and make sure that you **learn** those formulae that are not on it.
- If you cannot do a question, **leave it out** and **go back** to it at the end.
- Keep an eye on the time. Allow enough time to check through your answers.
- If you finish early, check through everything very carefully and try to fill in any gaps.
- Try to write something even if you are not sure about it. Leaving an empty space will score you no marks.

Good luck!

Number revision

Multiple-choice questions

Choose just one answer, a, b, c or d. Circle your choice.

1 Which of these is the largest number? 1469, 3271, 1059, 3276

   a) 1469   **b)** 3271   **c)** 1059   **d)** 3276   (1 mark)

2 What does the digit 7 in the number 34 718 stand for?

   a) 7 units   **b)** 7 tens   **c)** 7 hundreds   **d)** 7 thousands   (1 mark)

3 Which number is fifty-two thousand, four hundred and six written in figures?

   a) 52 406   **b)** 54 206   **c)** 52 460   **d)** 5246   (1 mark)

4 What is the third multiple of 7?

   a) 7   **b)** 14   **c)** 21   **d)** 28   (1 mark)

5 Here are some cards.   3   7   6   4

   What is the **smallest** number you can make with these cards?

   a) 7643   **b)** 3764   **c)** 3674   **d)** 3467   (1 mark)

Score   / 5

Short-answer questions

Answer all parts of each question.

1 Write these numbers in words.

   a) 602 _____ (1 mark)

   b) 5729 _____ (1 mark)

2 Write these numbers in figures.

   a) Four hundred and thirty-six _____ (1 mark)

   b) Six million, four hundred and five _____ (1 mark)

3 What value does the digit 3 represent in each of these numbers?

   a) 739 _____ (1 mark)

   b) 83 147 _____ (1 mark)

   c) 346 295 _____ (1 mark)

4 Arrange these numbers in order of size, **smallest** first.

   a) 47, 6, 93, 827, 1436, 75, 102 _____ (2 marks)

   b) 159, 3692, 4207, 4138, 729, 4879 _____ (2 marks)

Score   / 11

GCSE-style questions

Answer all parts of the questions. Show your workings (on a separate sheet of paper if necessary) and include the correct units in your answers.

1 Here is a list of numbers.

17   170   1700   17 000   170 000   1 700 000

Write down the number from the list that is...

a) seventeen hundred _____ (1 mark)

b) one hundred and seventy thousand _____ (1 mark)

2 a) Write the number sixteen thousand, four hundred and thirty-one in figures.

_____ (1 mark)

b) Write down the value of the 3 in the number 532 146.

_____ (1 mark)

c) Write down the **smallest even number** that can be made from these cards.

(3)   (5)   (2)   (8) _____ (1 mark)

3 This table shows the amount of money raised from five charity events.

Charity event	Amount
Dance festival	£1061
Battle of the Bands	£974
Sponsored run	£2712
Non-uniform day	£1361
Cake baking	£572

a) What is the amount of money raised in the dance festival? Write down the amount in words.

_____ (1 mark)

b) How much more did the sponsored run raise than the cake baking?

_____ (2 marks)

4 Write these numbers in order of size, **smallest** first.

a) i) 61, 104, 18, 130, 72

_____ (1 mark)

ii) 19, 62, 407, 397, 18

_____ (1 mark)

b) Write down a multiple of 3 between 13 and 16.

_____ (1 mark)

Score   / 11

Number

How well did you do?

| 0–8 | Try again | 9–15 | Getting there | 16–22 | Good work | 23–27 | Excellent! |

For more information on this topic, see pages 4–7 of your Success Revision Guide.

7

Types of numbers

Multiple-choice questions

Choose just one answer, a, b, c or d. Circle your choice.

1 What is the positive square root of 81?

   a) 7   **b)** -9   **c)** -7   **d)** 9   **(1 mark)**

2 What is the reciprocal of $\frac{7}{4}$?

   a) $\frac{7}{4}$ **b)** $\frac{4}{7}$ **c)** 7   **d)** 4   **(1 mark)**

3 What is the value of 4^2?

   a) 12   **b)** 16   **c)** 4   **d)** 64   **(1 mark)**

4 Work out the value of $\sqrt[3]{27}$.

   a) 9   **b)** 6   **c)** 3   **d)** 81   **(1 mark)**

5 What is the highest common factor of 18 and 24?

   a) 6   **b)** 18   **c)** 12   **d)** 432   **(1 mark)**

Score   / 5

Short-answer questions

Answer all parts of each question.

1 State whether each statement is **true** or **false**.

   a) 2 is the only even prime number.   **(1 mark)**

   b) 12 is a factor of 6.   **(1 mark)**

   c) 9 is a factor of 3.   **(1 mark)**

   d) 1, 2, 4, 6, 12, 24 are the only factors of 24.   **(1 mark)**

2 Work out the answers to these questions.

   a) $\sqrt{4} =$ _____   **b)** $\sqrt{100} =$ _____   **c)** $4^3 =$ _____

   d) $\sqrt[3]{8} =$ _____   **e)** $\sqrt[3]{-125} =$ _____   **f)** $9^2 =$ _____   **(6 marks)**

3 Write 72 as a product of its prime factors. _____   **(2 marks)**

4 The number 180 is written as a product of its prime factors. What are the values of a and b?

$180 = 2^a \times 3^b \times 5$ _____   **(2 marks)**

5 What is the least common multiple of 20 and 30? _____   **(1 mark)**

6 What is the highest common factor of 24 and 40? _____   **(1 mark)**

7 Decide whether this statement is **true** or **false**.

$\frac{5}{6}$ is the reciprocal of $1\frac{1}{5}$ _____   **(1 mark)**

Score   / 17

GCSE-style questions

Answer all parts of the questions. Show your workings (on a separate sheet of paper if necessary) and include the correct units in your answers.

1 Some numbers are in the cloud below. Choose numbers from the cloud to answer the questions below.

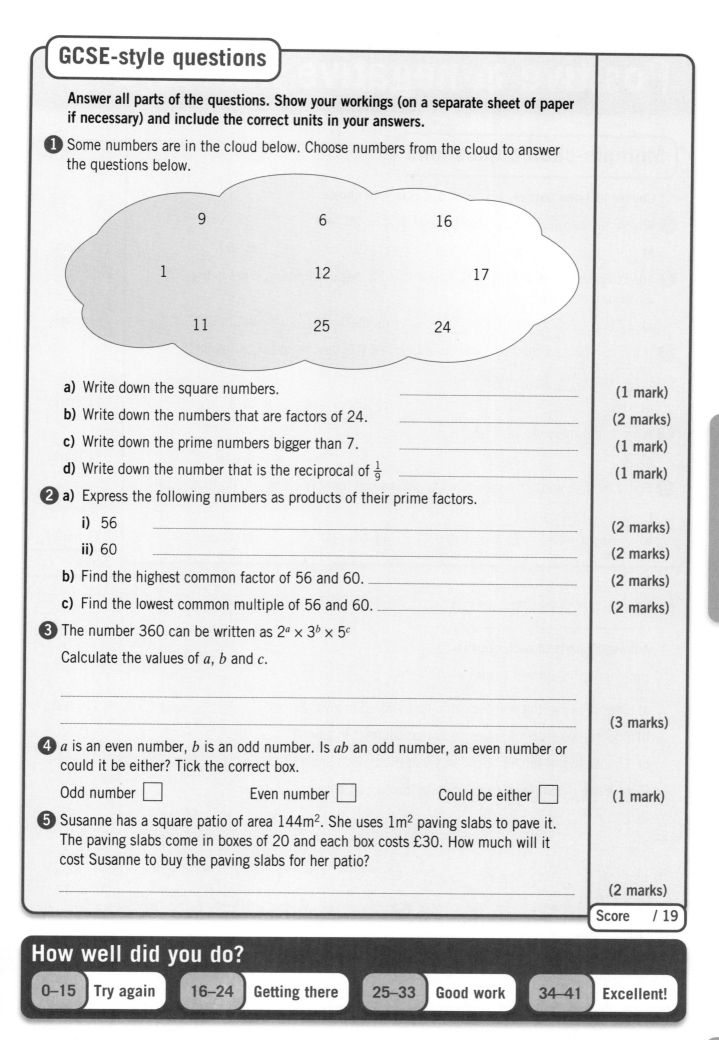

9   6   16

1   12   17

11   25   24

    a) Write down the square numbers. _____ (1 mark)

    b) Write down the numbers that are factors of 24. _____ (2 marks)

    c) Write down the prime numbers bigger than 7. _____ (1 mark)

    d) Write down the number that is the reciprocal of $\frac{1}{9}$ _____ (1 mark)

2 **a)** Express the following numbers as products of their prime factors.

    i) 56 _____ (2 marks)

    ii) 60 _____ (2 marks)

    b) Find the highest common factor of 56 and 60. _____ (2 marks)

    c) Find the lowest common multiple of 56 and 60. _____ (2 marks)

3 The number 360 can be written as $2^a \times 3^b \times 5^c$

Calculate the values of a, b and c.

_____

_____ (3 marks)

4 a is an even number, b is an odd number. Is ab an odd number, an even number or could it be either? Tick the correct box.

Odd number ☐   Even number ☐   Could be either ☐   (1 mark)

5 Susanne has a square patio of area 144m². She uses 1m² paving slabs to pave it. The paving slabs come in boxes of 20 and each box costs £30. How much will it cost Susanne to buy the paving slabs for her patio?

_____ (2 marks)

Score   / 19

Number

How well did you do?

0–15 **Try again**   16–24 **Getting there**   25–33 **Good work**   34–41 **Excellent!**

For more information on this topic, see pages 4–5 of your Success Revision Guide.

Positive & negative numbers

Multiple-choice questions

Choose just one answer, a, b, c or d. Circle your choice.

1 Which number in this list is the **largest**? 7, 11, -20, -41

    a) 7   **b)** 11   **c)** -20   **d)** -41   **(1 mark)**

2 The temperature outside is -5°C. Inside it is 28 degrees warmer. What is the temperature inside?

    a) 17°C   **b)** 21°C   **c)** 23°C   **d)** 25°C   **(1 mark)**

3 If the numbers on the two cards are multiplied together, what is the answer?

    [-3]   [5]

    a) -15   **b)** 2   **c)** 15   **d)** 8   **(1 mark)**

4 What is the value of -12 + (-6)?

    a) -6   **b)** -20   **c)** 6   **d)** -18   **(1 mark)**

5 Some number cards are shown below. Which two number cards add up to give 1?

    [-7]   [4]   [9]   [-3]

    a) -7 and 4   **b)** 4 and -3   **c)** 9 and 4   **d)** -7 and -3   **(1 mark)**

Score   / 5

Short-answer questions

Answer all parts of each question.

1 Here are some number cards.   [-7]   [0]   [5]   [-3]

    a) Choose two of the number cards that add up to give -2. ....   **(1 mark)**

    b) Choose two of the number cards that subtract to give -4. ....   **(1 mark)**

    c) Choose two of the number cards that multiply to give -15. ....   **(1 mark)**

2 Draw a line to join each calculation to the correct answer.

-3 × 4	10
12 ÷ (-2)	-1
-4 – (-3)	-12
-5 × (-2)	4
-20 ÷ (-5)	-6

    (5 marks)

3 Work out the answers to the following questions.

    a) (-40) ÷ (-4) = ...   **b)** -7 + (-3) = ...   **c)** 8 – (-6) = ...   **(3 marks)**

④ Here are some numbers in a number pyramid.
The number in each rectangle is found
by adding the two numbers below.
Complete the number pyramid.

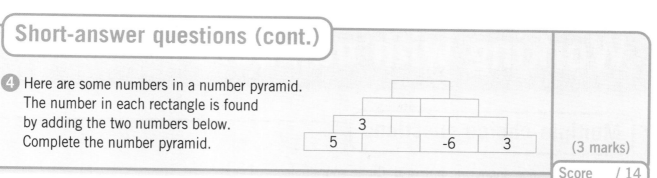

(3 marks)

GCSE-style questions

Answer all parts of the questions. Show your workings (on a separate sheet of paper if necessary) and include the correct units in your answers.

❶ The temperatures at midnight in various cities on one night in December are shown in the table below.

City	Temperature (°C)
Cairo	4
London	-2
New York	-7
Oslo	-14

a) How many degrees warmer is Cairo than Oslo? _____ °   (1 mark)

b) i) On the same night, the temperature in Sydney is 24 degrees warmer than in New York. What is the temperature in Sydney?

_____ °C   (2 marks)

ii) How many degrees colder is it in London than in Sydney?

_____ °C   (2 marks)

❷ One evening last winter, the temperature in Swansea was 4°C, in Manchester it was -2°C and in Glasgow it was -8°C.

a) Work out the difference in temperature between Swansea and Glasgow.

_____ degrees   (1 mark)

b) The temperature in Manchester increased by 6 degrees. Work out the new temperature in Manchester.

_____ °C   (1 mark)

c) The temperature in Glasgow fell by 3 degrees. Work out the new temperature in Glasgow.

_____ °C   (1 mark)

Score   / 8

Number

How well did you do?

| 0–6 | Try again | 7–14 | Getting there | 15–21 | Good work | 22–27 | Excellent! |

For more information on this topic, see pages 6–7 of your Success Revision Guide.

Working with numbers

Multiple-choice questions

Choose just one answer, a, b, c or d. Circle your choice.

1 Work out the answer to 27×100.

a) 27   **b)** 2700   **c)** 270   **d)** 27 000   (1 mark)

2 Work out the answer to $81 \div 1000$.

a) 81   **b)** 0.81   **c)** 0.081   **d)** 8.1   (1 mark)

3 Work out the answer to $274 + 639$.

a) 913   **b)** 931   **c)** 879   **d)** 874   (1 mark)

4 Work out the answer to $1479 - 387$.

a) 1192   **b)** 1092   **c)** 1112   **d)** 1012   (1 mark)

5 Work out the answer to 379×6.

a) 2072   **b)** 2174   **c)** 3274   **d)** 2274   (1 mark)

Score   / 5

Short-answer questions

Answer all parts of each question.

1 Draw a line from each calculation to the correct answer.

6×10	2400
70×1000	70 000
$240 \div 100$	60
$600 \div 1000$	2.4
80×30	0.6

(5 marks)

2 Work out the following calculations, showing all your working.

a) $379 + 42 =$ _____   **b)** $639 - 274 =$ _____

c) $5296 \times 3 =$ _____   **d)** $2496 \div 3 =$ _____

(4 marks)

3 Work out the following calculations, showing all your working.

a) $279 \times 26 =$ _____   **b)** $159 \times 48 =$ _____

c) $323 \div 19 =$ _____   **d)** $1296 \div 27 =$ _____

(4 marks)

4 A shop buys 142 sweaters. If each sweater is sold for £62, how much money does the shop take in total?

_____

_____

(2 marks)

Score   / 15

Answer all parts of the questions. Show your workings (on a separate sheet of paper if necessary) and include the correct units in your answers.

1 The table shows the cost of three types of paper. Simon buys one pack of plain paper and one pack of lined paper. He pays with a £10 note.

Plain paper	£2.15
Squared paper	£1.95
Lined paper	£2.70

a) How much change should he get?

_____ (4 marks)

b) Shezad wants to buy some packs of squared paper. He has £25 to spend. What is the greatest number of packs of squared paper he can buy?

_____ (2 marks)

2 Three teachers are planning to take some students to the zoo. Adult tickets cost £18.80 and student tickets cost £14.20. There is a budget of £555 for the tickets. Work out the greatest number of students that can go to the zoo.

_____

_____ (3 marks)

3 a) Here is Jackie's shopping bill. Complete the totals.

Item	Cost	Number bought	Total cost
Bread	79p	4	
Milk	72p	2	
Cleaning fluid	£2.76	2	

(3 marks)

b) Jackie pays using a £5 voucher and the remainder in cash. How much cash does she use?

_____ (1 mark)

4 Mrs Sharpe is printing a test for all year 10 students. Each test uses 16 sheets of paper.

a) There are 186 students in year 10. How many sheets of paper does she need?

_____ (3 marks)

b) A ream contains 500 sheets of paper. How many reams of paper does she need to print all the tests?

_____ (2 marks)

Score   / 18

Number

How well did you do?

| 0–13 | Try again | 14–22 | Getting there | 23–32 | Good work | 33–38 | Excellent! |

For more information on this topic, see pages 8–9 of your Success Revision Guide.

Fractions

Multiple-choice questions

Choose just one answer, a, b, c or d. Circle your choice.

1 In a class of 24 students, $\frac{3}{8}$ wear glasses. How many students wear glasses?

    a) 9   **b)** 6   **c)** 3   **d)** 12   (1 mark)

2 Which one of these fractions is equivalent to $\frac{5}{9}$?

    a) $\frac{16}{27}$ **b)** $\frac{9}{18}$ **c)** $\frac{25}{45}$ **d)** $\frac{21}{36}$ (1 mark)

3 Work out the answer to $\frac{5}{9} - \frac{1}{3}$

    a) $\frac{1}{3}$ **b)** $\frac{2}{9}$ **c)** $\frac{4}{6}$ **d)** $\frac{4}{12}$ (1 mark)

4 Work out the answer to $\frac{2}{11} \times \frac{7}{9}$

    a) $\frac{14}{11}$ **b)** $\frac{14}{9}$ **c)** $\frac{14}{99}$ **d)** $\frac{2}{99}$ (1 mark)

5 Work out the answer to $\frac{3}{10} \div \frac{2}{5}$

    a) $\frac{3}{4}$ **b)** $\frac{6}{50}$ **c)** $\frac{6}{15}$ **d)** $\frac{4}{3}$ (1 mark)

Score   / 5

Short-answer questions

Answer all parts of each question.

1 Fill in the blanks in these equivalent fractions.

    a) $\frac{2}{11} = \frac{4}{\underline{\quad}}$ **b)** $\frac{4}{7} = \frac{\overline{\quad}}{49}$ **c)** $\frac{25}{100} = \frac{1}{\underline{\quad}}$ **d)** $\frac{12}{17} = \frac{36}{\underline{\quad}}$ (4 marks)

2 Arrange these fractions in order of size, **smallest** first. (Hint: use common denominators where appropriate.)

    a) $\frac{2}{3}$ $\frac{4}{5}$ $\frac{1}{7}$ $\frac{3}{4}$ $\frac{1}{2}$ $\frac{3}{10}$

_____   (2 marks)

    b) $\frac{5}{8}$ $\frac{1}{3}$ $\frac{2}{7}$ $\frac{1}{9}$ $\frac{3}{4}$ $\frac{2}{5}$

_____   (2 marks)

3 State whether these statements are **true** or **false**.

    a) $\frac{4}{5}$ of 20 is bigger than $\frac{6}{7}$ of 14. _____   (1 mark)

    b) $\frac{2}{9}$ of 27 is smaller than $\frac{1}{3}$ of 15. _____   (1 mark)

4 Work out the answers to the following. Give your answers in the simplest form.

    a) $\frac{2}{9} + \frac{1}{3}$ ___   **b)** $\frac{7}{11} - \frac{1}{4}$ ___   **c)** $\frac{4}{7} \times \frac{3}{8}$ ___   **d)** $\frac{9}{12} \div \frac{1}{4}$ ___

    e) $\frac{5}{7} - \frac{1}{21}$ ___   **f)** $\frac{4}{9} + \frac{3}{27}$ ___   **g)** $\frac{7}{12} \times \frac{3}{2}$ ___   **h)** $\frac{11}{7} \div \frac{12}{7}$ ___   (8 marks)

5 Change these improper fractions to mixed numbers.

a) $\frac{5}{2}$ = _____

b) $\frac{5}{3}$ = _____

c) $\frac{9}{2}$ = _____

d) $\frac{12}{11}$ = _____

(4 marks)

Score   / 22

GCSE-style questions

Answer all parts of the questions. Show your workings (on a separate sheet of paper if necessary) and include the correct units in your answers.

1 Charlotte's take-home pay is £930. She gives her mother $\frac{1}{3}$ of this and spends $\frac{1}{5}$ of the £930 on going out. What fraction of the £930 is left? Give your answer as a fraction in its simplest form.

_____

(3 marks)

2 Phoebe says, 'Since 5 is halfway between 4 and 6 then $\frac{1}{5}$ will be halfway between $\frac{1}{4}$ and $\frac{1}{6}$.' Phoebe is wrong. Show that $\frac{1}{5}$ is not halfway between $\frac{1}{4}$ and $\frac{1}{6}$.

_____

_____

(3 marks)

3 There are 860 pupils in a school. 140 of these pupils are in year 8. What fraction of the 860 pupils are not in year 8? Give your fraction in its simplest form.

_____

(3 marks)

4 Thomas shares a bag of 30 sweets with his friends. He gives Jessica $\frac{2}{5}$ of his sweets and he gives Samuel $\frac{1}{6}$ of his sweets. He keeps the rest for himself. How many sweets does Thomas keep for himself?

Sweets

_____

(3 marks)

5 In a class of 32 pupils, $\frac{1}{8}$ are left-handed. How many students are not left-handed?

_____

(1 mark)

Score   / 13

Number

How well did you do?

| 0–11 | Try again | | 12–21 | Getting there | | 22–32 | Good work | | 33–40 | Excellent! |

For more information on this topic, see pages 10–11 of your Success Revision Guide.

Decimals

Multiple-choice questions

Choose just one answer, a, b, c or d. Circle your choice.

1 Round 18.629 to 2 decimal places.

   a) 18.69   **b)** 18.63   **c)** 18.7   **d)** 18.62   (1 mark)

2 Work out the answer to 9.45×5

   a) 47.52   **b)** 56.7   **c)** 47.25   **d)** 46.75   (1 mark)

3 Here are some discs. (5.8) (5.79) (5.81) (5.805)

   Which of the discs has the **largest** number?

   a) 5.8   **b)** 5.79   **c)** 5.81   **d)** 5.805   (1 mark)

4 If a piece of cheese weighs 0.3kg, how much would 70 identical pieces of cheese weigh?

   a) 2.1kg   **b)** 21kg   **c)** 0.21kg   **d)** 210kg   (1 mark)

5 Work out the answer to $520 \div 0.02$

   a) 2600   **b)** 260   **c)** 260 000   **d)** 26 000   (1 mark)

Score / 5

Short-answer questions

Answer all parts of each question.

1 Look at these statements and decide whether they are **true** or **false**.

   a) 12.204 is smaller than 12.214 .... (1 mark)

   b) 37.465 rounded to 1 decimal place is 37.5 .... (1 mark)

   c) 27.406 rounded to 2 decimal places is 27.41 .... (1 mark)

2 Four friends run a race. Their times, in seconds, are shown in the table below.

Harry	Hussain	Molly	Joshua
14.072	15.12	14.07	16.321

   a) Who won the race? .... (1 mark)

   b) What is the difference between Hussain and Joshua's times? .... (1 mark)

   c) How much faster was Molly than Harry? .... (1 mark)

3 Here are some calculations. Fill in the gaps to make the calculations correct.

   a) $640 \div 40 =$ _____   **b)** $500 \times 0.2 =$ _____   **c)** $600 \div 0.3 =$ _____

   d) $40 \div$ _____ $= 400$ **e)** _____ $\times 0.02 = 0.48$ **f)** $420 \div$ _____ $= 42\,000$ (6 marks)

Score / 12

GCSE-style questions

Answer all parts of the questions. Show your workings (on a separate sheet of paper if necessary) and include the correct units in your answers.

1 Here are some number cards.

[6.14] [7.29] [7.42] [7.208] [6.141]

a) Arrange the cards in order of size, **smallest** first.

( ) ( ) ( ) ( ) ( )

(2 marks)

b) Work out the difference between the largest and the smallest number.

_____

(1 mark)

c) What is the total value of all these cards? _____ (1 mark)

d) Round these cards to 2 decimal places.

[7.208] [6.141]

i) 7.208 becomes _____ **ii)** 6.141 becomes _____ (2 marks)

2 a) Write the number 0.629 as a fraction. _____ (1 mark)

b) Write $\frac{7}{25}$ as a decimal. _____ (1 mark)

3 a) Ryan has three pounds and forty pence. His friend, Dom, has two pounds and three pence. Write down in figures how much money Ryan and Dom each have.

Ryan: £ _____ Dom: £ _____ (2 marks)

b) Ryan writes down the total amount of money that he and Dom have as £5.7, but he is wrong. Explain why Ryan is wrong.

_____

(2 marks)

4 Matthew is putting a new fence down the side of his garden. The fence panels are 0.9 metres long. The total length of the fence needs to be 5.4 metres. Each fence panel costs £17.48. Work out how much it costs Matthew to put the fence down the side of his garden.

_____

(4 marks)

5 Here are some number cards.

[0.1] [0.01] [0.001] [100] [10]

Use one of the number cards to fill each gap to make the statements correct.

a) 60 ÷ _____ = 6000 (1 mark)

b) 25 × _____ = 2.5 (1 mark)

c) 720 ÷ _____ = 720 000 (1 mark)

Score   / 19

Number

How well did you do?

| 0–9 | Try again | 10–18 | Getting there | 19–28 | Good work | 29–36 | Excellent! |

For more information on this topic, see pages 12–15 of your Success Revision Guide.

Percentages 1

Multiple-choice questions

Choose just one answer, a, b, c or d. Circle your choice.

1 Work out 10% of £850.

   a) £8.50   **b)** £0.85   **c)** £85   **d)** £42.50   **(1 mark)**

2 Work out 17.5% of £60.

   a) £9   **b)** £15   **c)** £10.50   **d)** £12.50   **(1 mark)**

3 A CD player costs £45. In a sale, the price is reduced by 20%. What is the sale price of the CD player?

   a) £38   **b)** £40.50   **c)** £9   **d)** £36   **(1 mark)**

4 A sofa costs £850. In a sale, it is reduced by 30%. What is the sale price of the sofa?

   a) £255   **b)** £765   **c)** £85   **d)** £595   **(1 mark)**

5 In a survey, 17 people out of 25 said they preferred type A cola. What percentage of people preferred type A cola?

   a) 68%   **b)** 60%   **c)** 72%   **d)** 75%   **(1 mark)**

Score   / 5

Short-answer questions

Answer all parts of each question.

1 Draw a line from each calculation to the correct answer.

10% of 30	16
5% of 15	3
40% of 40	5
25% of 20	0.75

(4 marks)

2 12 out of 30 people wear glasses. What percentage wear glasses?

_____ %   **(2 marks)**

3 Last year, Colin earned £25 500. This year he has a 3% pay rise. How much does Colin now earn?

£ _____   **(2 marks)**

4 The cost of a parking ticket is £1.50. The price of the ticket rises by 20%. What is the cost of the parking ticket after the price increase?

£ _____   **(2 marks)**

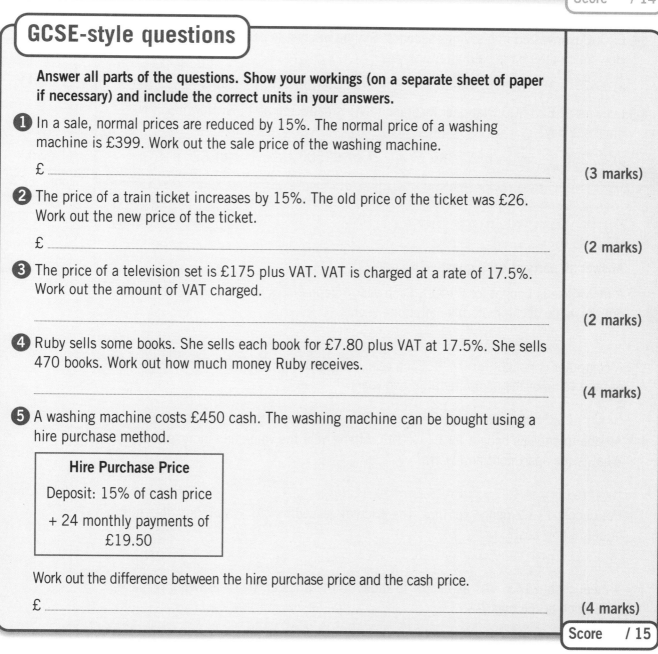

Short-answer questions (cont.)

⑤ Lucinda scored 58 out of 75 in a test. What percentage did she get? Give your answer to the nearest whole number.

_____ %   (2 marks)

⑥ A coat costs £120. In a sale, it is reduced by 15%. Work out the sale price of the coat.

£ _____   (2 marks)

Score   / 14

GCSE-style questions

Answer all parts of the questions. Show your workings (on a separate sheet of paper if necessary) and include the correct units in your answers.

❶ In a sale, normal prices are reduced by 15%. The normal price of a washing machine is £399. Work out the sale price of the washing machine.

£ _____   (3 marks)

❷ The price of a train ticket increases by 15%. The old price of the ticket was £26. Work out the new price of the ticket.

£ _____   (2 marks)

❸ The price of a television set is £175 plus VAT. VAT is charged at a rate of 17.5%. Work out the amount of VAT charged.

_____   (2 marks)

❹ Ruby sells some books. She sells each book for £7.80 plus VAT at 17.5%. She sells 470 books. Work out how much money Ruby receives.

_____   (4 marks)

❺ A washing machine costs £450 cash. The washing machine can be bought using a hire purchase method.

| **Hire Purchase Price** |
| Deposit: 15% of cash price |
| + 24 monthly payments of £19.50 |

Work out the difference between the hire purchase price and the cash price.

£ _____   (4 marks)

Score   / 15

How well did you do?

| 0–8 | Try again | 9–17 | Getting there | 18–25 | Good work | 26–34 | Excellent! |

For more information on this topic, see pages 16–17 of your Success Revision Guide.

Number

Percentages 2

Multiple-choice questions

Choose just one answer, a, b, c or d. Circle your choice.

1 A bike was bought for £120. Each year its value depreciated by 10%. What was the bike worth two years later?

a) £97.20   b) £98   c) £216   d) £110   **(1 mark)**

2 £2000 is invested in a savings account. Simple interest is paid at 2.1% per annum. How much interest is paid after one year?

a) £42   b) £5.20   c) £84.88   d) £84   **(1 mark)**

3 Lucy earns £23 500. National Insurance (NI) is deducted at 11%. How much NI must she pay?

a) £2250   b) £2585   c) £2500   d) £20 915   **(1 mark)**

Score   / 3

Short-answer questions

Answer all parts of each question.

1 A motorbike is bought for £9000. Each year it depreciates in value by 12%. Work out the value of the motorbike after one year.

£ ....   **(2 marks)**

2 A computer is bought for £799. Each year it depreciates in value by 30%. Work out the value of the computer after two years.

£ ....   **(2 marks)**

3 An apartment was bought for £112 000. After a year the value had increased by 8%. What is the apartment now worth?

£ ....   **(2 marks)**

4 Petrol cost 113.2 pence per litre. The price increased by 2%. How much does a litre of petrol now cost?

.... p   **(2 marks)**

5 A meal costs £143. VAT at 17.5% is added to the price of the meal. What is the final price of the meal?

£ ....   **(2 marks)**

6 VAT of 5% is added to a gas bill of £72. Find the total amount to be paid.

£ ....   **(2 marks)**

Score   / 12

20

GCSE-style questions

Answer all parts of the questions. Show your workings (on a separate sheet of paper if necessary) and include the correct units in your answers.

1 Find the simple interest on £2000 invested for two years at 4% per year.

_____

(3 marks)

2 A year ago, Matthew's height was 1.43 metres. His height has now increased by 12.3%. Work out Matthew's height now. Give your answer to an appropriate degree of accuracy.

_____

(3 marks)

3 Here is part of Melissa's gas bill.

```
         Gas Bill

New reading:    3838
Old reading:    2715
Cost per unit:  3.64p
VAT at 5%
```

Work out the total cost of the gas bill including VAT at 5%.

_____

_____

(5 marks)

4 Work out 40% of £2500.

_____

(2 marks)

5 Nigel opened an account at his local bank with £450. After one year, the bank paid him interest. He then had £465.75 in his account.

a) Work out, as a percentage, his local bank's interest rate.

_____

(3 marks)

b) Lucy opened a bank account. She invested £700 for two years at 4% compound interest. How much money did she have in her account after two years?

_____

(3 marks)

6 Last year, Rupinder earned £26 500. She does not have to pay income tax on £9500 of these earnings of £26 500. She has to pay income tax at 20% on all her earnings above £9500. Work out how much income tax Rupinder has to pay.

_____

(3 marks)

Score   / 22

Number

How well did you do?

| 0–11 | Try again | 12–19 | Getting there | 20–28 | Good work | 29–37 | Excellent! |

For more information on this topic, see pages 18–19 of your Success Revision Guide.

Fractions, decimals & percentages

Multiple-choice questions

Choose just one answer, a, b, c or d. Circle your choice.

1 What is $\frac{3}{5}$ as a percentage?

  a) 30%   **b)** 25%   **c)** 60%   **d)** 75%   (1 mark)

2 What is $\frac{2}{3}$ written as a decimal?

  a) 0.77   **b)** 0.$\dot{6}$ **c)** 0.665   **d)** 0.6   (1 mark)

3 What is the **smallest** value in this list of numbers? 29%, 0.4, $\frac{3}{4}$, $\frac{1}{8}$

  a) 29%   **b)** 0.4   **c)** $\frac{3}{4}$ **d)** $\frac{1}{8}$ (1 mark)

4 What is the **largest** value in this list of numbers? $\frac{4}{5}$, 80%, $\frac{2}{3}$, 0.9

  a) $\frac{4}{5}$ **b)** 80%   **c)** $\frac{2}{3}$ **d)** 0.9   (1 mark)

5 Change $\frac{5}{8}$ into a decimal.

  a) 0.625   **b)** 0.425   **c)** 0.125   **d)** 0.725   (1 mark)

Score   / 5

Short-answer questions

Answer all parts of each question.

1 The table shows equivalent fractions, decimals and percentages. Fill in the gaps.

Fraction	Decimal	Percentage
$\frac{2}{5}$		
		5%
	0.$\dot{3}$	
	0.04	
		25%
$\frac{1}{8}$		

(6 marks)

2 Put these cards in order of size, **smallest** first.

0.37	30%	$\frac{3}{8}$	$\frac{1}{3}$	92%	$\frac{1}{2}$	0.62

(2 marks)

3 A sundial is being sold in two different garden centres. The cost of the sundial is £89.99 in both garden centres. Both garden centres have a promotion.

Gardens Are Us (Sundial 22% off)   Rosebushes (Sundial $\frac{1}{4}$ off)

In which garden centre is the sundial **cheaper**? Explain your answer.

_____

_____

(2 marks)

Score   / 10

GCSE-style questions

Answer all parts of the questions. Show your workings (on a separate sheet of paper if necessary) and include the correct units in your answers.

1 Place these seven numbers in order of size, **smallest** first.

25%, $\frac{1}{3}$, 0.27, $\frac{2}{5}$, 0.571, 72%, $\frac{1}{8}$ _____

(3 marks)

2 Decide whether these calculations give the same answer for this instruction: increase £40 by 20%.

Jack says: (Multiply 40 by 1.2)   Hannah says: (Work out 10%, double it and then add 40)

Explain your reasoning.

_____

(2 marks)

3 Philippa is buying a new television. She sees three different advertisements for the same television set.

Ed's Electricals
TV normal price
£250
Sale 10% off

Sheila's Bargains
TV £185 plus
VAT at $17\frac{1}{2}$%

GITA's TV SHOP
Normal price
£290
Sale: $\frac{1}{5}$ off normal price

Philippa wants to buy her television from one of these shops, as cheaply as possible. Which shop should she choose and how much cheaper is it than the most expensive shop?

_____

(5 marks)

Score   / 10

How well did you do?

0–7 Try again   8–13 Getting there   14–20 Good work   21–25 Excellent!

For more information on this topic, see page 20 of your Success Revision Guide.

23

Approximations & using a calculator

Multiple-choice questions

Choose just one answer, a, b, c or d. Circle your choice.

1 Round 5379 to 3 significant figures.

   a) 538   **b)** 5370   **c)** 537   **d)** 5380   (1 mark)

2 Estimate the answer to the calculation 27×41.

   a) 1107   **b)** 1200   **c)** 820   **d)** 1300   (1 mark)

3 A carton of orange juice costs 79p. Estimate the cost of 402 cartons of orange juice.

   a) £350   **b)** £250   **c)** £400   **d)** £320   (1 mark)

4 A school trip is organised. 396 pupils are going on the trip. Each coach seats 50 pupils. Approximately how many coaches are needed?

   a) 12   **b)** 5   **c)** 8   **d)** 10   (1 mark)

5 Estimate the answer to the calculation $\frac{(4.2)^2}{107}$

   a) 16   **b)** 1.6   **c)** 0.16   **d)** 160   (1 mark)

Score   / 5

Short-answer questions

Answer all parts of each question.

1 State whether each statement is **true** or **false**.

   a) 2.742 rounded to 3 significant figures is 2.74   (1 mark)

   b) 2793 rounded to 2 significant figures is 27   (1 mark)

   c) 32 046 rounded to 1 significant figure is 40 000   (1 mark)

   d) 14.637 rounded to 3 significant figures is 14.6   (1 mark)

2 Mount Everest is 8850m high. What is this height correct to 2 significant figures?

                                                  (1 mark)

3 Work out the following, giving your answers to 3 significant figures.

   a) $\frac{4.2 \times (3.6 + 5.1)}{2 - 1.9}$ **b)** $6 \times \sqrt{\frac{12.1}{4.2}}$

   c) $\frac{12^5}{4.3 \times 9.15}$ (3 marks)

4 Round each of the numbers in the following calculations to 1 significant figure, then work out an approximate answer.

   a) $\frac{(32.9)^2}{9.1}$ (1 mark)

   b) $\frac{(906 \div 31.4)^2}{7.1 + 2.9}$ (1 mark)

5 Tim works in a bookshop. He earns £5.95 per hour. One week, Tim works 21 hours. Approximately how much does Tim earn in that week?

_____

(2 marks)

Score   / 12

GCSE-style questions

Answer all parts of the questions. Show your workings (on a separate sheet of paper if necessary) and include the correct units in your answers.

1 a) Use your calculator to work out the value of the following expression. Write down all the figures on your calculator display.

$$\frac{(15.2 + 6.9)^2}{3.63 - 4.2}$$ _____

(2 marks)

b) Round your answer to 3 significant figures. _____

(1 mark)

2 Use your calculator to work out the value of the following to 3 significant figures.

$$\frac{\sqrt{4.9^2 + 6.3}}{2.1 \times 0.37}$$ _____

(3 marks)

3 Freddie is laying laminate flooring in his office. The area of the floor space in his office is 375m². Each strip of laminate covers an area of 2m². Each laminate pack contains 16 strips and costs £17.50. How much does it cost Freddie to buy the laminate flooring for his office?

_____

(3 marks)

4 a) Use your calculator to work out the value of the following. Write down all the figures on your calculator display.

$$\frac{27.1 \times 6.2}{38.2 - 9.9}$$ _____

(2 marks)

b) Round each of the numbers in the above calculation to 1 significant figure and obtain an approximate answer.

_____

(3 marks)

5 a) Write down two numbers you could use to get an approximate answer to 31×79.

_____ and _____

(1 mark)

b) Work out your approximate answer. _____

(1 mark)

c) Work out the difference between your approximate answer and the exact answer.

_____

(2 marks)

6 Estimate the following, leaving your answer as an improper fraction in its simplest form.

$$\frac{21.2^2 - 10.3^2}{3.6 \times 29}$$ _____

(3 marks)

Score   / 21

Number

How well did you do?

| 0–14 | Try again | 15–22 | Getting there | 23–30 | Good work | 31–38 | Excellent! |

For more information on this topic, see pages 21–23 of your Success Revision Guide.

Ratio

Multiple-choice questions

Choose just one answer, a, b, c or d. Circle your choice.

1 What is the ratio 6 : 18 written in its simplest form?

   a) 3 : 1   **b)** 3 : 9   **c)** 1 : 3   **d)** 9 : 3   (1 mark)

2 Write the ratio 200 : 500 in its simplest form.

   a) 20 : 50   **b)** 1 : 5   **c)** 1 : 25   **d)** 2 : 5   (1 mark)

3 If £140 is divided in the ratio 3 : 4, what is the size of the larger share?

   a) £45   **b)** £60   **c)** £80   **d)** £90   (1 mark)

4 A recipe for 4 people needs 800g of flour. How much flour is needed for 6 people?

   a) 12g   **b)** 120g   **c)** 12kg   **d)** 1200g   (1 mark)

5 If 9 oranges cost £1.08, how much would 14 similar oranges cost?

   a) £1.50   **b)** £1.68   **c)** £1.20   **d)** £1.84   (1 mark)

Score   / 5

Short-answer questions

Answer all parts of each question.

1 Write down each of the following ratios in the form 1 : n

   a) 10 : 30 _____   **b)** 6 : 24 _____   **c)** 9 : 27 _____   (3 marks)

2 10 bottles of lemonade have a total capacity of 1680ml. Work out the total capacity of 7 similar bottles.

_____ ml   (1 mark)

3 **a)** Increase £4.10 in the ratio 2 : 5 _____   (1 mark)

   b) Decrease 120g in the ratio 5 : 2 _____   (1 mark)

4 Mrs London inherited £55 000. She divided the money between her children in the ratio 3 : 3 : 5. How much did the child with the largest share receive?

£ _____   (2 marks)

5 It takes 6 people 3 days to dig and lay a cable. How long would it take 4 people? (All people work at the same rate.)

_____ days   (2 marks)

6 If £1 = 1.10 euros (€), change £250 into euros.

€ _____   (2 marks)

Score   / 12

GCSE-style questions

Answer all parts of the questions. Show your workings (on a separate sheet of paper if necessary) and include the correct units in your answers.

1 7 metres of rope costs £5.46. Work out the cost of 13 metres of the same rope.

_____ (2 marks)

2 It takes 3 builders 16 days to build a wall. How long would it take 8 builders to build a wall of the same size? (All the builders work at the same rate.)

_____ days (3 marks)

3 Mineral water is sold in two sizes.

Which size of bottle gives the better value for money?
You must show all of your working.

Water 1 litre   £1.52

Water 25cl   39p

_____

_____ (2 marks)

4 Tia went on holiday to Florida. The exchange rate was £1 = 1.65 American dollars ($).

a) Tia changed £750 into American dollars. How many dollars did Tia have?

$ _____ (2 marks)

b) When Tia returned from holiday she had $245 left. The exchange rate had fallen and on the day she exchanged the dollars for pounds, the rate was £1 = $1.49. Work out how much Tia got in pounds. Give your answer to the nearest penny.

£ _____ (2 marks)

5 Vicky and Tracy share £14 400 in the ratio 4 : 5. How much does each of them receive?

Vicky: £ _____   Tracy: £ _____ (3 marks)

6 James uses these ingredients to make 12 buns:

| 50g butter, 40g sugar, 2 eggs, 45g flour, 15ml milk |

James wants to make 30 similar buns. Write down how much of each ingredient he needs for 30 buns.

Butter _____ g   Sugar _____ g

Eggs _____   Flour _____ g

Milk _____ ml

(3 marks)

Score   / 17

How well did you do?

| 0–8 | Try again | 9–17 | Getting there | 18–26 | Good work | 27–34 | Excellent! |

For more information on this topic, see pages 24–25 of your Success Revision Guide.

Number

27

Indices

Multiple-choice questions

Choose just one answer, a, b, c or d. Circle your choice.

1. In index form, what is the value of $8^3 \times 8^{11}$?

   a) 8^{14} **b)** 8^{33} **c)** 64^{14} **d)** 64^{33} (1 mark)

2. In index form, what is the value of $4^2 \times 4^3$?

   a) 12^2 **b)** 4^5 **c)** 4^6 **d)** 16^6 (1 mark)

3. In index form, what is the value of $(3^4)^2$?

   a) 3^6 **b)** 9^8 **c)** 9^4 **d)** 3^8 (1 mark)

4. What is the value of $2^3 \times 3^2$?

   a) 36   **b)** 54   **c)** 48   **d)** 72   (1 mark)

5. In index form, what is the value of $7^{12} \div 7^2$?

   a) 7^{10} **b)** 7^6 **c)** 7^{14} **d)** 7^{24} (1 mark)

Score   / 5

Short-answer questions

Answer all parts of each question.

1. Work out the exact value of the following:

   a) 4^3 _____   **b)** 2^5 _____   **c)** 3^4 _____   **d)** $(2^3)^2$ _____   (4 marks)

2. State whether each of these expressions is **true** or **false**.

   a) $a^4 \times a^5 = a^{20}$ _____   **b)** $2a^4 \times 3a^2 = 5a^8$ _____

   c) $10a^6 \div 2a^4 = 5a^2$ _____   **d)** $20a^4b^2 \div 10a^5b = \dfrac{2b}{a}$ _____

   e) $7^3 \times 7^4 = 7^{12}$ _____   **f)** $4^1 = 4$ _____   (6 marks)

3. Simplify the following expressions.

   a) $3a \times 2a =$ _____   **b)** $12m^3 \div 4m =$ _____

   c) $10a^2b^4 \times 2ab =$ _____   **d)** $n^7 \times n^9 =$ _____

   e) $(a^4)^3 =$ _____   **f)** $12a^4 \div 16a^7 =$ _____

   g) $4a^5 \times 3a^6 =$ _____   **h)** $12b^3 \div 4b =$ _____   (8 marks)

4. Find the value of n in each of the following equations.

   a) $8^{10} \times 8^n = 8^{16}$ _____   **b)** $10^n \div 10^2 = 10^{12}$ _____

   c) $5^n = 5$ _____   (3 marks)

Score   / 21

Answer all parts of the questions. Show your workings (on a separate sheet of paper if necessary) and include the correct units in your answers.

1 a) Work out the value of the following:

    i) 4^2 _____   **ii)** 3^3 _____   (2 marks)

    b) Write the following as a power of 9: $9 \times 9 \times 9 \times 9 \times 9$ _____   (1 mark)

2 Simplify the following:

    a) $p^3 \times p^4$ _____   (1 mark)

    b) $\dfrac{n^7}{n^3}$ _____   (1 mark)

    c) $\dfrac{a^3 \times a^4}{a}$ _____   (1 mark)

    d) $\dfrac{12a^2 b}{3a}$ _____   (1 mark)

    e) $(3a)^2$ _____   (1 mark)

3 Work out the value of the following:

    a) 3^1 _____   (1 mark)

    b) 5^2 _____   (1 mark)

    c) $3^4 \times 2^3$ _____   (1 mark)

4 a) Evaluate the following:

    i) 8^1 _____   (1 mark)

    ii) 6^2 _____   (1 mark)

    iii) $2^3 \times 2^2$ _____   (1 mark)

    b) Write this expression as a single power of 5.

      $\dfrac{5^7 \times 5^3}{5^6}$ _____   (2 marks)

    c) Evaluate $(3^2)^2$ _____   (1 mark)

5 Simplify the following:

    a) $2a^3 \times 3a^2$ _____   (1 mark)

    b) $\dfrac{12a^2 b}{4ab}$ _____   (1 mark)

    c) $\dfrac{b^6 \times 3b^2}{12b^{10}}$ _____   (1 mark)

6 Evaluate the following:

    a) i) 7^2 _____   **ii)** $3^2 \times 3^3$ _____   **iii)** $4^7 \div 4^5$ _____   (3 marks)

    b) Write $\dfrac{3^4 \times 3^6}{3^2}$ as a single power of 3. _____   (2 marks)

Score   / 25

Number

How well did you do?

| 0–12 | Try again | 13–26 | Getting there | 27–40 | Good work | 41–51 | Excellent! |

For more information on this topic, see pages 26–27 of your Success Revision Guide.

Algebra

Multiple-choice questions

Choose just one answer, a, b, c or d. Circle your choice.

1 What is the expression $4a + 3b - a + 6b$ when it is fully simplified?

  a) $9b - 3a$ **b)** $3a - 9b$ **c)** $3a + 9b$ **d)** $5a + 9b$ **(1 mark)**

2 What is the expression $7a - 4b + 6a - 3b$ when it is fully simplified?

  a) $7b - a$ **b)** $13a + 7b$ **c)** $a - 7b$ **d)** $13a - 7b$ **(1 mark)**

3 What is the expression $3(2x - 1)$ when it is multiplied out?

  a) $6x - 3$ **b)** $6x - 1$ **c)** $2x - 3$ **d)** $6x + 3$ **(1 mark)**

4 Factorise fully the expression $25x + 15$.

  a) $5(5x + 15)$ **b)** $25(x + 15)$ **c)** $5(5x + 3)$ **d)** $5(5x)$ **(1 mark)**

5 What is the expression $5(n - 3)$ when it is multiplied out?

  a) $5n - 3$ **b)** $5n + 15$ **c)** $3n - 5$ **d)** $5n - 15$ **(1 mark)**

Score   / 5

Short-answer questions

Answer all parts of each question.

1 State whether these simplified expressions are **true** or **false**.

  a) $3a - 2b + 5a + b = 8a - b$ **(1 mark)**

  b) $6ay - 3ay^2 + 2ay^2 - 4ay = 2ay - ay^2$ **(1 mark)**

  c) $3ab + 2a^2b - a^2b + 4ba = a^2b + 12a^2 + b^2$ **(1 mark)**

2 Choose an expression from the cards to make each of the calculations below correct.

  $\boxed{3n - 3}$ $\boxed{8(n + 2)}$ $\boxed{n^2 + 3n}$ $\boxed{n^2 + 2}$ $\boxed{5(n + 3)}$ $\boxed{3n - 9}$

  a) $3(n - 3) = $ _____   **b)** $5n + 15 = $ _____

  c) $n(n + 3) = $ _____   **d)** $8n + 16 = $ _____   **(4 marks)**

3 Factorise the following expressions.

  a) $10n + 15$ _____   **b)** $24 - 36n$ _____

  c) $5 + 10n$ _____   **d)** $20 - 4n$ _____

  e) $6a^2 + 12a$ _____   **(5 marks)**

Score   / 12

Answer all parts of the questions. Show your workings (on a separate sheet of paper if necessary) and include the correct units in your answers.

1 Here is a table for a two-stage number machine. It multiplies by 4 and subtracts 2. Complete the missing numbers in the table.

× 4 – 2	
Input	Output
1	2
2	6
4	....
6	....
....	34

(3 marks)

2 a) Simplify $t + t$.

....

(1 mark)

b) Simplify $y^2 + y^2 + y^2$.

....

(1 mark)

3 a) Simplify fully $7n - 4n + 3n$. ....

(1 mark)

b) Simplify fully $3a \times 2b$. ....

(1 mark)

4 a) Expand and simplify $6x - 2(x - 2)$.

....

(2 marks)

b) i) Factorise $6a + 12$. ....

(1 mark)

ii) Factorise completely $10a^2 - 15ab$. ....

(2 marks)

5 Show that $n(n + 2) - 3(n - 1)$ simplifies to $n^2 - n + 3$.

....

....

(3 marks)

6 a) Expand and simplify $2(3a - 1) - (a - 2)$.

....

(2 marks)

b) Factorise fully the following expressions.

i) $3n - 12$ ....

(1 mark)

ii) $8pq - 12p$ ....

(1 mark)

Score   / 19

Algebra

How well did you do?

| 0–10 | Try again | 11–18 | Getting there | 19–28 | Good work | 29–36 | Excellent! |

For more information on this topic, see pages 30–31 of your Success Revision Guide.

31

Equations 1

Multiple-choice questions

Choose just one answer, a, b, c or d. Circle your choice.

1. Solve the equation $4n - 2 = 10$.

   a) $n = 4$ **b)** $n = 2$ **c)** $n = 3$ **d)** $n = 3.5$ (1 mark)

2. Solve the equation $\frac{n}{2} + 4 = 2$.

   a) $n = -4$ **b)** $n = 4$ **c)** $n = 12$ **d)** $n = -12$ (1 mark)

3. Solve the equation $4(x + 3) = 16$.

   a) $x = 9$ **b)** $x = 7$ **c)** $x = 4$ **d)** $x = 1$ (1 mark)

4. Solve the equation $4(n + 2) = 8(n - 3)$.

   a) $n = 16$ **b)** $n = 8$ **c)** $n = 4$ **d)** $n = 12$ (1 mark)

5. Solve the equation $10 - 6n = 4n - 5$.

   a) $n = 2$ **b)** $n = -2$ **c)** $n = 1.5$ **d)** $n = -1.5$ (1 mark)

Score   / 5

Short-answer questions

Answer all parts of each question.

1. Solve the following equations.

   a) $n - 3 = 6$ **b)** $n + 10 = 12$

   c) $3n - 1 = 5$ **d)** $5 - n = 12$

   e) $\frac{n}{6} = 3$ **f)** $5n + 1 = 6$ (6 marks)

2. Reece thinks of a number. He adds 4 to the number. He then multiplies by 5. His answer is 25. What number did Reece think of?

   (2 marks)

3. Solve the following equations.

   a) $5n = 25$ **b)** $\frac{36}{n} = 12$

   c) $2n - 4 = 10$ **d)** $3 - 2n = 14$

   e) $\frac{n}{5} + 2 = 7$ **f)** $4 - \frac{n}{2} = 2$ (6 marks)

4. Solve the following equations.

   a) $12n + 5 = 3n + 32$ **b)** $5n - 4 = 3n + 6$

   c) $5(n + 1) = 25$ **d)** $4(n - 2) = 3(n + 2)$ (4 marks)

Score   / 18

GCSE-style questions

Answer all parts of the questions. Show your workings (on a separate sheet of paper if necessary) and include the correct units in your answers.

1 Solve these equations.

a) $3n = 12$ .... (2 marks)

b) $5n + 3 = 18$ .... (3 marks)

c) $3(n + 2) = 21$ .... (3 marks)

d) $\frac{n-2}{4} = 3$ .... (2 marks)

2 Solve these equations.

a) $5m - 3 = 12$ .... (2 marks)

b) $8p + 3 = 9 - 2p$ .... (2 marks)

c) $5(x - 1) = 3x + 7$ .... (2 marks)

d) $4 + x = 2(x - 1)$ .... (2 marks)

3 Each expression in the wall is formed by adding the two supporting expressions from the row below.

For example,

$4x + 7$	
$3x + 5$	$x + 2$

$3x + 5 + x + 2 = 4x + 7$

Use the wall below to find the value of x.

	6	
$2x + 5$		
$x + 1$	$x + 4$	$2x - 12$

.... (3 marks)

4 Sophie thinks of a number. She adds 9 to the number. She then multiplies the result by 4. Her answer is 60. What number did Sophie first think of?

....

.... (2 marks)

5 Solve $8 - 2x = 3x + 3$.

....

.... (3 marks)

Score _____ / 26

Algebra

How well did you do?

| 0–18 | Try again | 19–31 | Getting there | 32–46 | Good work | 47–49 | Excellent! |

For more information on this topic, see pages 32–33 of your Success Revision Guide.

Equations 2 & inequalities

Multiple-choice questions

Choose just one answer, a, b, c or d. Circle your choice.

1 $-4 \leqslant y < 2$ and y is an integer. What are all the possible values of y?

  a) -4, -3, -2, -1, 0, 1, 2   **b)** -3, -2, -1, 0, 1, 2

  c) -4, -3, -2, -1, 0, 1   **d)** -3, -2, -1, 0, 1   **(1 mark)**

2 $-6 \leqslant 2n < 2$ and n is an integer. What are all the possible values of n?

  a) -6, -5, -4, -3, -2, -1, 0, 1   **b)** -3, -2, -1, 0, 1

  c) -3, -2, -1, 0   **d)** -2, -1, 0, 1, 2   **(1 mark)**

3 The equation $y^3 + 2y = 82$ has a solution between 4 and 5. By using a method of trial and improvement, find the solution to 1 decimal place. 🖩

  a) 3.9   **b)** 4.1   **c)** 4.2   **d)** 4.3   **(1 mark)**

4 Solve the inequality $3x + 1 < 19$.

  a) $x < 3$ **b)** $x < 7$ **c)** $x < 5$ **d)** $x < 6$ **(1 mark)**

5 Solve the inequality $2x - 7 < 9$.

  a) $x < 9$ **b)** $x < 10$ **c)** $x < 8$ **d)** $x < 6.5$ **(1 mark)**

Score   **/ 5**

Short-answer questions

Answer all parts of each question.

1 The angles in a triangle add up to 180°. Form an equation using n and solve it.

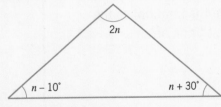

                      $n = $ _____   **(2 marks)**

2 Solve the following inequalities.

  a) $5x + 2 < 12$ _____   **b)** $\frac{x}{3} + 1 \geqslant 3$ _____

  c) $3 \leqslant 2x + 1 \leqslant 9$ _____   **d)** $3 \leqslant 3x + 2 \leqslant 8$ _____   **(4 marks)**

3 Use a trial and improvement method to solve the following equation. Give your answer to 1 decimal place. 🖩

  $t^2 - 2t = 20$ $t = $ _____ or $t = $ _____   **(2 marks)**

Score   **/ 8**

Answer all parts of the questions. Show your workings (on a separate sheet of paper if necessary) and include the correct units in your answers.

1 The lengths, in cm, of the sides of the triangle are $2x + 7$, $3x - 1$ and $4x + 6$.

The perimeter of the triangle is 39cm. Work out the length of the shortest side of the triangle.

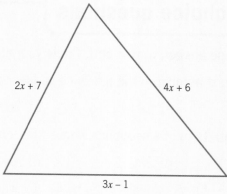

....

....

(4 marks)

2 n is an integer.

a) Write down the values of n that satisfy the inequality $-4 < n \leqslant 2$.

....

(2 marks)

b) Solve the inequality $5p - 2 \leqslant 8$.

....

(2 marks)

3 Use the method of trial and improvement to solve the equation $x^3 + 3x = 28$. Give your answer correct to 1 decimal place. You must show all your working. 🖩

....

....

....

$x = $ ....

(4 marks)

4 The equation $x^3 + 10x = 51$ has a solution between 2 and 3. Use the method of trial and improvement to find this solution. Give your answer correct to 1 decimal place. You must show all your working. 🖩

....

....

$x = $ ....

(4 marks)

Score   / 16

Algebra

How well did you do?

| 0–6 | Try again | 7–14 | Getting there | 15–22 | Good work | 23–29 | Excellent! |

For more information on this topic, see pages 34–37 of your Success Revision Guide.

35

Number patterns & sequences

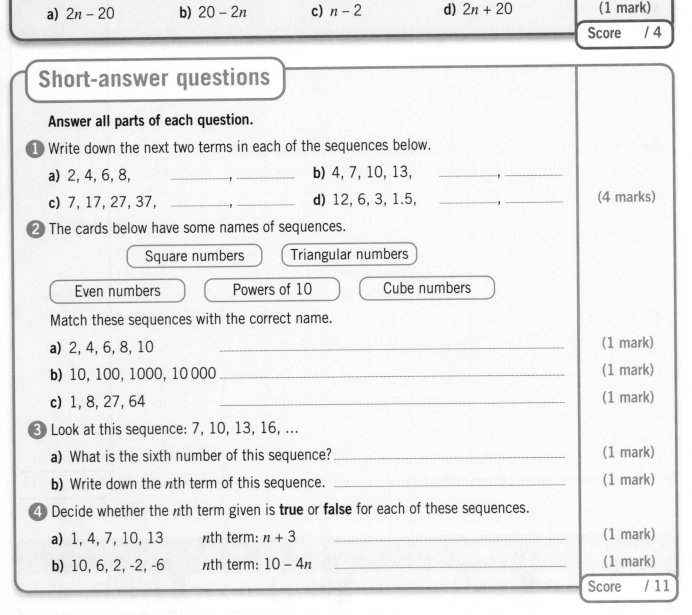

Multiple-choice questions

Choose just one answer, a, b, c or d. Circle your choice.

1 What is the next number in the following sequence? 1, 4, 9, 16, ...

    a) 24   **b)** 49   **c)** 36   **d)** 25   (1 mark)

2 What is the nth term of a sequence whose first four terms are 5, 7, 9, 11?

    a) $2n + 3$ **b)** $2n - 3$ **c)** $n + 2$ **d)** $3 - 2n$ (1 mark)

3 If the nth term of a sequence is given by $4 - 3n$, what is the fifth term of this sequence?

    a) -8   **b)** -2   **c)** -11   **d)** -14   (1 mark)

4 What is the nth term of a sequence whose first four terms are 18, 16, 14, 12?

    a) $2n - 20$ **b)** $20 - 2n$ **c)** $n - 2$ **d)** $2n + 20$ (1 mark)

Score   / 4

Short-answer questions

Answer all parts of each question.

1 Write down the next two terms in each of the sequences below.

    a) 2, 4, 6, 8, ..., ...   **b)** 4, 7, 10, 13, ..., ...

    c) 7, 17, 27, 37, ..., ...   **d)** 12, 6, 3, 1.5, ..., ...   (4 marks)

2 The cards below have some names of sequences.

    (Square numbers)   (Triangular numbers)

    (Even numbers)   (Powers of 10)   (Cube numbers)

Match these sequences with the correct name.

    a) 2, 4, 6, 8, 10   ....   (1 mark)

    b) 10, 100, 1000, 10 000   ....   (1 mark)

    c) 1, 8, 27, 64   ....   (1 mark)

3 Look at this sequence: 7, 10, 13, 16, ...

    a) What is the sixth number of this sequence? ....   (1 mark)

    b) Write down the nth term of this sequence. ....   (1 mark)

4 Decide whether the nth term given is **true** or **false** for each of these sequences.

    a) 1, 4, 7, 10, 13 nth term: $n + 3$ ....   (1 mark)

    b) 10, 6, 2, -2, -6 nth term: $10 - 4n$ ....   (1 mark)

Score   / 11

Algebra

36

Answer all parts of the questions. Show your workings (on a separate sheet of paper if necessary) and include the correct units in your answers.

1 Here are some patterns made up of dots:

1   2   3   4

a) In the space below, draw pattern number 5.

(1 mark)

b) Complete the table.

Pattern number	1	2	3	4	5	6
Number of dots	10	14	18	22		

(1 mark)

c) How many dots would be used in pattern number 12? _____ (1 mark)

2 Here are the first four numbers of a simple sequence: 5, 7, 9, 11, …

a) Write down the next two numbers of the sequence. _____ (2 marks)

b) Write down, in words, the rule to continue this sequence.

_____ (1 mark)

3 a) Here are the first five terms of a sequence: 64, 32, 16, 8, 4, …

Write down the next three terms of the sequence. _____, _____, _____ (3 marks)

b) Here are the first five terms of a different sequence: 2, 7, 12, 17, 22, …
Find, in terms of n, an expression for the nth term for this sequence.

_____ (2 marks)

4 Here are the first four numbers of a sequence: 3, 7, 11, 15, …
Write down, in terms of n, the nth term for this sequence.

_____ (2 marks)

5 Charlotte says, 'The nth term of the sequence 3, 5, 7, 9, … is $2n - 1$ since they are odd numbers.' Explain whether Charlotte is correct.

_____ (2 marks)

Score   / 15

How well did you do?

| 0–7 | Try again | 8–15 | Getting there | 16–24 | Good work | 25–30 | Excellent! |

For more information on this topic, see pages 36–37 of your Success Revision Guide.

Algebra

Formulae

Multiple-choice questions

Choose just one answer, a, b, c or d. Circle your choice.

1 If $a = \frac{b}{c}$ and $b = 12$ and $c = 4$, what is the value of a?

   a) 12   **b)** 4   **c)** 6   **d)** 3   **(1 mark)**

2 If $m = \sqrt{\frac{r^2 p}{4}}$ and $r = 3$ and $p = 6$, what is the positive value of m to 1 decimal place? ▦

   a) 13.5   **b)** 182.3   **c)** 3.7   **d)** 3   **(1 mark)**

3 There are n books in a pile. Each book is 5cm thick. What is the formula for the total height, h, of the pile of books?

   a) $5n$ **b)** $h = 5n$ **c)** $h = \frac{n}{5}$ **d)** $h = \frac{5}{n}$ **(1 mark)**

4 Rearrange the formula $a = b + 4c$ to make c the subject.

   a) $c = \frac{a+b}{4}$ **b)** $c = a + 4b$ **c)** $c = \frac{a-b}{4}$ **d)** $c = 4b + a$ **(1 mark)**

5 Rearrange the formula $P = 5a + b$ to make a the subject.

   a) $a = \frac{P-b}{5}$ **b)** $a = \frac{P+b}{5}$ **c)** $a = 5P + b$ **d)** $a = 5P - b$ **(1 mark)**

Score   / 5

Short-answer questions

Answer all parts of each question.

1 $F = ma$ is a formula. **True** or **false**? .... **(1 mark)**

2 $a = \frac{b^2 + 2c}{4}$

   a) Calculate a if $b = 2$ and $c = 6$. .... **(1 mark)**

   b) Calculate a if $b = 3$ and $c = -2$. .... **(1 mark)**

   c) Calculate b if $a = 25$ and $c = 18$. .... **(1 mark)**

3 Rearrange each of the formulae below to make b the subject.

   a) $p = 3b - 4$ .... **(1 mark)**

   b) $y = \frac{ab - 6}{4}$ .... **(1 mark)**

   c) $5(n + b) = 2b + 2$ .... **(1 mark)**

4 John buys b books costing £6 each and m magazines costing 67 pence each. Write down a formula for the total cost (T) of the books and magazines.

   $T = $ .... **(2 marks)**

Score   / 9

Answer all parts of the questions. Show your workings (on a separate sheet of paper if necessary) and include the correct units in your answers.

1 Using algebra, write the following as an equation: 'To find p, multiply n by 5 and then subtract 6.'

.... **(1 mark)**

2 A babysitting service advertises its rates as shown below.

> **Busy Babies**
> Baby and toddler babysitting service (0 to 5 years old)
> Cost = number of hours × £6.50 + taxi fare

a) How much would it cost to hire a babysitter from 6pm to 11pm, when the taxi fare for the babysitter was £11.50?

.... **(2 marks)**

b) Mrs. Samuels paid 'Busy Babies' £28.75 to look after her small child for 3 hours. How much was the taxi fare?

.... **(2 marks)**

3 A shop sells white and brown bread. A loaf of white bread costs w pence and a loaf of brown bread costs b pence. James buys four loaves of white bread and five loaves of brown bread for his café. The total cost is C pence. Write down a formula for C in terms of w and b.

.... **(3 marks)**

4 Imran and Sophie use this rule to work out their pay:

> Pay = number of hours worked × amount paid per hour

a) Last week, Imran worked for 27 hours. He was paid £5.70 per hour. What was Imran's pay? 🖩

.... **(2 marks)**

b) Last week, Sophie's pay was £192.20. She was paid £6.20 per hour. For how many hours did Sophie work? 🖩

.... **(2 marks)**

5 A person's body mass index (BMI), b, is calculated using the formula $b = \frac{m}{h^2}$ where m is the person's mass in kilograms and h is their height in metres. A person is classed as overweight if their BMI is greater than 25. Peter has a height of 184cm and a mass of 89.5kg. Would Peter be classed as overweight? You must show working to justify your answer. 🖩

.... **(3 marks)**

Score   / 15

Algebra

How well did you do?

| 0–8 | **Try again** | 9–17 | **Getting there** | 18–22 | **Good work** | 23–29 | **Excellent!** |

For more information on this topic, see pages 38–39 of your Success Revision Guide.

39

Straight-line graphs

Multiple-choice questions

Choose just one answer, a, b, c or d. Circle your choice.

Questions 1–3 refer to the diagram opposite.

1 What are the coordinates of point A?

a) (4, 2)   b) (2, 4)

c) (-2, 1)   d) (1, -3)   (1 mark)

2 What are the coordinates of point B?

a) (4, 2)   b) (0, -3)   c) (1, -3)   d) (-3, 1)   (1 mark)

3 What are the coordinates of point C?

a) (-2, 0)   b) (0, -2)   c) (2, 0)   d) (-3, 1)   (1 mark)

4 What point lies on the line $x = 2$?

a) (1, 3)   b) (2, 3)   c) (3, 2)   d) (0, 2)   (1 mark)

5 What point lies on the line $y = -3$?

a) (-3, 5)   b) (5, -2)   c) (-2, 5)   d) (5, -3)   (1 mark)

Score   / 5

Short-answer questions

Answer all parts of each question.

1 What is the gradient of the line $y = 3 + 4x$? _____   (1 mark)

2 a) i) Complete the table of values for $y = 6 - x$.

x	-2	-1	0	1	2
$y = 6 - x$	_____	_____	6	_____	4

(2 marks)

ii) On the grid below, plot your values for x and y. Join the points with a straight line.   (1 mark)

b) A second line goes through the coordinates (1, 5), (-2, -4) and (2, 8).

i) Draw this line on the grid.   (1 mark)

ii) Write down the gradient of the line you have just drawn.

_____

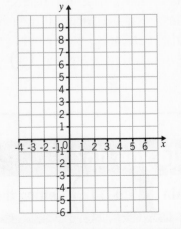

c) What are the coordinates of the point where the two lines meet?

_____   (2 marks)

(1 mark)

Score   / 8

40

Answer all parts of the questions. Show your workings (on a separate sheet of paper if necessary) and include the correct units in your answers.

1 The line with equation $x + y = 4$ has been drawn on the grid.

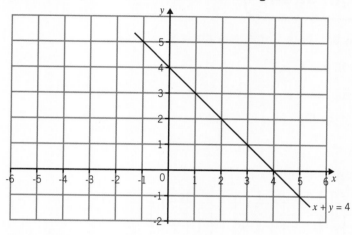

a) Write down the gradient of the line $x + y = 4$.

....

(3 marks)

b) On the grid above, draw the graph with the equation $y = 2x - 2$.

(3 marks)

c) Write down the coordinates of the point of intersection of the two straight-line graphs.

(..................., ...)

(1 mark)

2 a) Complete the table of values for $y = 2x - 3$.

x	-2	-1	0	1	2
y	-7	....	-3	....	....

(2 marks)

b) On the grid below, draw the graph of $y = 2x - 3$.

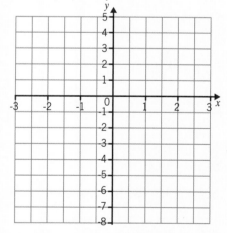

(2 marks)

Score   / 11

Algebra

For more information on this topic, see pages 34–35 and 40–41 of your Success Revision Guide.

Curved graphs

Multiple-choice questions

Choose just one answer, a, b, c or d. Circle your choice.

1 What point lies on the graph $y = x^2 - 2$?

a) (1, 1)   **b)** (4, 14)   **c)** (2, 4)   **d)** (0, 2)   **(1 mark)**

2 On which of these curves does the point (2, 5) lie?

a) $y = x^2 - 4$ **b)** $y = 2x^2 + 3$ **c)** $y = x^2 - 6$ **d)** $y = 2x^2 - 3$ **(1 mark)**

Questions 3–5 refer to these diagrams:

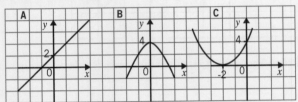

3 What is the equation of graph A?

a) $y = 5 - 2x^2$ **b)** $y = x^2 + 4x + 4$ **c)** $y = x + 2$ **d)** $y = 4 - x^2$ **(1 mark)**

4 What is the equation of graph B?

a) $y = 5 - 2x^2$ **b)** $y = x^2 + 4x + 4$ **c)** $y = x + 2$ **d)** $y = 4 - x^2$ **(1 mark)**

5 What is the equation of graph C?

a) $y = 5 - 2x^2$ **b)** $y = x^2 + 4x + 4$ **c)** $y = x + 2$ **d)** $y = 4 - x^2$ **(1 mark)**

Score   / 5

Short-answer questions

Answer all parts of each question.

1 a) Complete the table of values for $y = x^2 - 2x - 2$.

x	-2	-1	0	1	2	3
$y = x^2 - 2x - 2$			-2			1

(2 marks)

b) On the grid below, draw the graph of $y = x^2 - 2x - 2$.   **(3 marks)**

c) Use your graph to write down an estimate for...

i) the solutions of the equation $x^2 - 2x - 2 = -2$

$x =$ _____ and $x =$ _____   **(2 marks)**

ii) the solutions of the equation $x^2 - 2x - 2 = 0$.

$x =$ _____ and $x =$ _____   **(2 marks)**

Score   / 9

GCSE-style questions

Answer all parts of the questions. Show your workings (on a separate sheet of paper if necessary) and include the correct units in your answers.

1 **a)** Complete the table of values for the graph $y = x^2 + 4$.

x	-3	-2	-1	0	1	2	3
$y = x^2 + 4$	13		5				13

(2 marks)

b) On the grid, draw the graph of $y = x^2 + 4$.

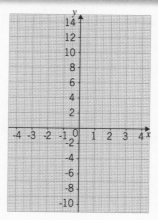

(2 marks)

c) Use your graph to find an estimate of...

i) the solution of the equation $x^2 + 4 = 10$

$x =$ _____

(1 mark)

ii) the solution of the equation $x^2 + 4 = 13$.

$x =$ _____

(2 marks)

2 **a)** Complete the table of values for the graph $y = x^3 + 1$.

x	-2	-1	0	1	2
$y = x^3 + 1$		0			9

(2 marks)

b) On the grid, draw the graph of $y = x^3 + 1$.

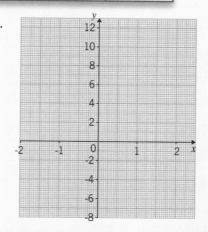

(2 marks)

Score   / 11

For more information on this topic, see pages 42–43 of your Success Revision Guide.

Algebra

Interpreting graphs

Multiple-choice questions

Choose just one answer, a, b, c or d. Circle your choice.

1 If £1 = $1.48, how much would £10 be in American dollars?

a) $0.148   b) $148   c) $14.80   d) $1480   **(1 mark)**

Questions 2–4 refer to the graph opposite.
The graph shows Mrs Morgan's car journey.

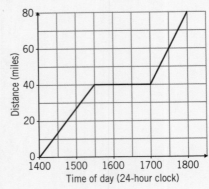

2 At what speed did Mrs Morgan travel for the first hour and a half?

a) 25mph   b) 28mph   c) 30mph   d) 26.7mph   **(1 mark)**

3 At what time did Mrs Morgan take a break from her car journey?

a) 1530   b) 1600   c) 1400   d) 1500   **(1 mark)**

4 At what speed did Mrs Morgan travel between 1700 and 1800 hours?

a) 60mph   b) 80mph   c) 35mph   d) 40mph   **(1 mark)**

Score   / 4

Short-answer questions

Answer all parts of each question.

1 Water is poured into these odd-shaped vases at a
constant rate. Match each vase to the correct graph.

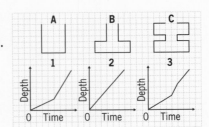

Vase A matches graph ....

Vase B matches graph ....

Vase C matches graph ....

(3 marks)

2 Match these graphs to the statements.

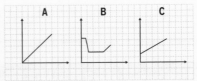

A mobile phone company charges a standard fee
plus a certain amount per call. Graph ....

The price of shares dropped sharply, levelled
off and then started rising. Graph ....

Conversion between kilometres and miles.
Graph ....

(3 marks)

Score   / 6

Algebra

Answer all parts of the questions. Show your workings (on a separate sheet of paper if necessary) and include the correct units in your answers.

1 The graph shows the cost, C (£) that a plumber charges for a number of hours, h.

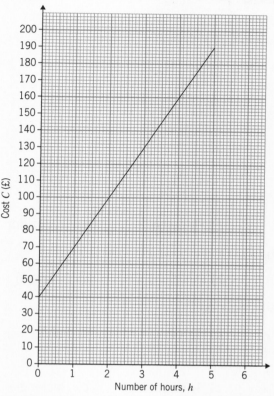

a) Circle the correct formula connecting the cost, C, and the number of hours, h, that the plumber works.

   $C = 3h + 40$ $C = 30h + 40$ $C = 40h + 30$ (1 mark)

b) Work out the price the plumber will charge if he works for...

   i) 2 hours

   .... (1 mark)

   ii) 4 hours 40 minutes (note all part hours are rounded to the next hour).

   ....

   .... (2 marks)

c) If the plumber works for 8 hours, Mrs. Robinson thinks she will be charged £280. Explain whether Mrs. Robinson is correct.

   ....

   .... (2 marks)

Score   / 6

Algebra

How well did you do?

| 0–4 | Try again | 5–8 | Getting there | 9–12 | Good work | 13–16 | Excellent! |

For more information on this topic, see pages 44–45 of your Success Revision Guide.

Shapes

Multiple-choice questions

Choose just one answer, a, b, c or d. Circle your choice.

Questions 1–5 refer to the diagrams below.

A   B   C   D

1 What is the name of shape B?

  a) Triangle   **b)** Kite   **c)** Hexagon   **d)** Trapezium   (1 mark)

2 What special type of triangle is shape A?

  a) Equilateral   **b)** Scalene   **c)** Isosceles   **d)** Isolateral   (1 mark)

3 How many lines of symmetry does shape C have?

  a) One   **b)** Two   **c)** Three   **d)** Four   (1 mark)

4 What is the name of shape C?

  a) Parallelogram   **b)** Kite   **c)** Trapezium   **d)** Rectangle   (1 mark)

5 What is the name of shape D?

  a) Triangle   **b)** Parallelogram   **c)** Hexagon   **d)** Pentagon   (1 mark)

Score   / 5

Short-answer questions

Answer all parts of each question.

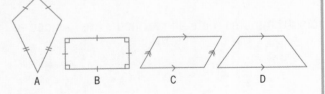

1 These shapes are quadrilaterals. State whether each of these statements is **true** or **false**.

A   B   C   D

  a) Shape B is a rectangle.   _____ (1 mark)

  b) Shape D is a parallelogram.   _____ (1 mark)

  c) Shape A has two lines of symmetry.   _____ (1 mark)

  d) Shape B has rotational symmetry of order 4.   _____ (1 mark)

  e) Shape C is a parallelogram.   _____ (1 mark)

2 a) How many lines of symmetry does a regular octagon have?

  _____ (1 mark)

  b) What is the order of rotational symmetry of a regular hexagon? _____ (1 mark)

Score   / 7

46

Answer all parts of the questions. Show your workings (on a separate sheet of paper if necessary) and include the correct units in your answers.

1 The diagram shows parts of a circle.

Choose the correct label for each part of the circle.

Radius
Circumference
Diameter
Arc

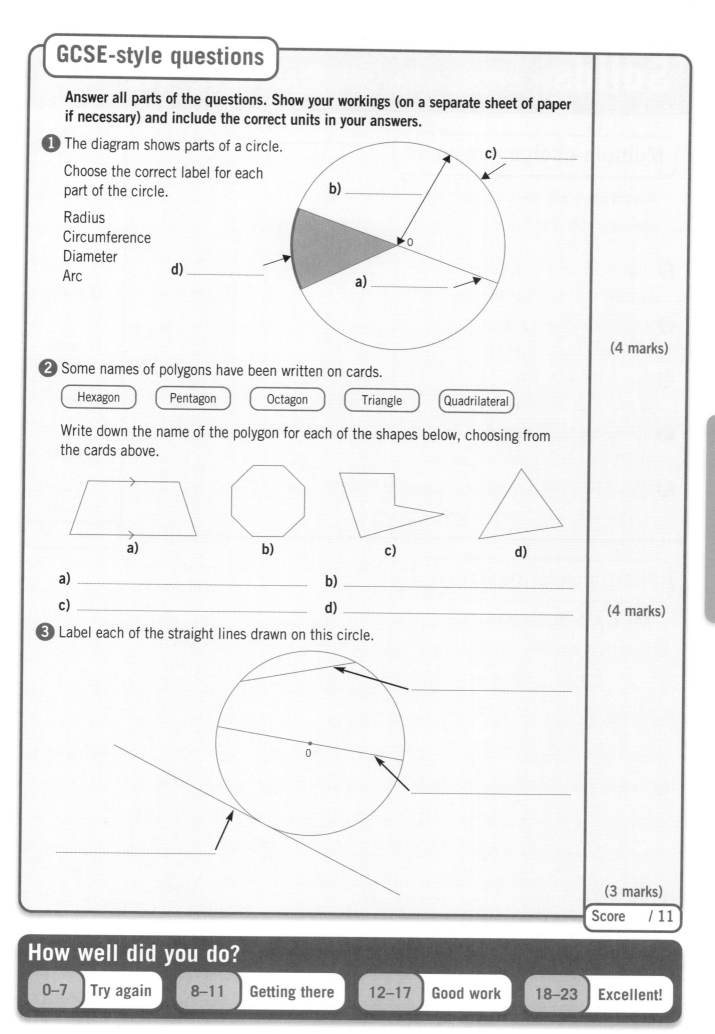

c) ....

b) ....

d) ....

a) ....

(4 marks)

2 Some names of polygons have been written on cards.

| Hexagon | Pentagon | Octagon | Triangle | Quadrilateral |

Write down the name of the polygon for each of the shapes below, choosing from the cards above.

a)   b)   c)   d)

a) ....   b) ....

c) ....   d) ....

(4 marks)

3 Label each of the straight lines drawn on this circle.

(3 marks)

Score   / 11

How well did you do?

| 0–7 | Try again | 8–11 | Getting there | 12–17 | Good work | 18–23 | Excellent! |

For more information on this topic, see pages 48–49 of your Success Revision Guide.

Geometry and measures

47

Solids

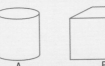

Multiple-choice questions

Choose just one answer, a, b, c or d. Circle your choice.

Questions 1–5 refer to the diagrams opposite.

1 What is the name of shape C?

   a) Cube   **b)** Cuboid   **c)** Cone   **d)** Cylinder   **(1 mark)**

2 What is the name of shape D?

   a) Cube   **b)** Sphere   **c)** Cuboid   **d)** Cone   **(1 mark)**

3 What is the name of shape A?

   a) Rhombus   **b)** Cone   **c)** Cylinder   **d)** Sphere   **(1 mark)**

4 How many edges does shape B have?

   a) 12   **b)** 8   **c)** 9   **d)** 10   **(1 mark)**

5 If you draw a plan of shape A, what shape will it be?

   a) Pentagon   **b)** Heptagon   **c)** Circle   **d)** Rectangle   **(1 mark)**

Score   / 5

Short-answer questions

Answer all parts of each question.

1 In the spaces below, write down the correct mathematical name of each object.

  a) _____   **b)** _____   **c)** _____   **(3 marks)**

2 On a separate piece of isometric paper, draw accurately a 2cm × 3cm × 4cm cuboid.

(3 marks)

3 Which of the following nets would make a cube?

     A   B   C   D   E

_____

(1 mark)

Score   / 7

Success

GCSE Mathematics
Foundation
Workbook Answers

Answers

Number

Page 6 – Number revision

Multiple-choice questions
1. d
2. c
3. a
4. c
5. d

Short-answer questions
1. a) Six hundred and two
   b) Five thousand, seven hundred and twenty-nine
2. a) 436
   b) 6 000 405
3. a) 3 tens
   b) 3 thousands
   c) 3 hundred thousands
4. a) 6, 47, 75, 93, 102, 827, 1436
   b) 159, 729, 3692, 4138, 4207, 4879

GCSE-style questions
1. a) 1700
   b) 170 000
2. a) 16 431
   b) 3 ten thousands = 30 000
   c) 2358
3. a) One thousand and sixty one pounds
   b) £2140
4. a) i) 18, 61, 72, 104, 130
      ii) 18, 19, 62, 397, 407
   b) 15

Page 8 – Types of numbers

Multiple-choice questions
1. d
2. b
3. b
4. c
5. a

Short-answer questions
1. a) True
   b) False
   c) False
   d) False
2. a) ±2
   b) ±10
   c) 64
   d) 2
   e) -5
   f) 81
3. $2^3 \times 3^2$
4. $a = 2, b = 2$
5. 60
6. 8
7. True

GCSE-style questions
1. a) 1, 9, 16, 25
   b) 1, 6, 12, 24
   c) 11, 17
   d) 9
2. a) i) $56 = 2 \times 2 \times 2 \times 7$
      ii) $60 = 2 \times 2 \times 3 \times 5$
   b) HCF = 4
   c) LCM = 840

3. $360 = 2^3 \times 3^2 \times 5$
   Hence $a = 3, b = 2, c = 1$
4. Even
5. £240

Page 10 – Positive & negative numbers

Multiple-choice questions
1. b
2. c
3. a
4. d
5. b

Short-answer questions
1. a) -7 and 5
   b) -7 and -3
   c) 5 and -3
2. -3×4 → 10
   $12 \div (-2)$ → -1
   $-4 - (-3)$ → -12
   $-5 \times (-2)$ → 4
   $-20 \div (-5)$ → -6
3. a) 10
   b) -10
   c) 14
4.

		-16		
	-5		-11	
	3	-8	-3	
5	-2	-6	3	

GCSE-style questions
1. a) 18°C
   b) i) 17°C
      ii) 19°C
2. a) 12 degrees
   b) 4°C
   c) -11°C

Page 12 – Working with numbers

Multiple-choice questions
1. b
2. c
3. a
4. b
5. d

Short-answer questions
1. 6×10 → 2400
   70×1000 → 70 000
   $240 \div 100$ → 60
   $600 \div 1000$ → 2.4
   80×30 → 0.6
2. a) 421
   b) 365
   c) 15 888
   d) 832
3. a) 7254
   b) 7632
   c) 17
   d) 48
4. £8804

GCSE-style questions
1. a) £5.15
   b) 12 packs of squared paper
2. 35 students

3. a)

Item	Cost	Number bought	Total cost
Bread	79p	4	£3.16
Milk	72p	2	£1.44
Cleaning fluid	£2.76	2	£5.52

   b) £5.12
4. a) 2976 sheets of paper
   b) 6 reams of paper

Page 14 – Fractions

Multiple-choice questions
1. a
2. c
3. b
4. c
5. a

Short-answer questions
1. a) 22
   b) 28
   c) 4
   d) 51
2. a) $\frac{1}{7}$ $\frac{3}{10}$ $\frac{1}{2}$ $\frac{2}{3}$ $\frac{3}{4}$ $\frac{4}{5}$
   b) $\frac{1}{9}$ $\frac{2}{7}$ $\frac{1}{3}$ $\frac{2}{5}$ $\frac{5}{8}$ $\frac{3}{4}$
3. a) True
   b) False
4. a) $\frac{5}{9}$
   b) $\frac{17}{44}$
   c) $\frac{3}{14}$
   d) 3
   e) $\frac{2}{3}$
   f) $\frac{5}{9}$
   g) $\frac{7}{8}$
   h) $\frac{11}{12}$
5. a) $2\frac{1}{2}$
   b) $1\frac{2}{3}$
   c) $4\frac{1}{2}$
   d) $1\frac{1}{11}$

GCSE-style questions
1. $\frac{7}{15}$
2. $\frac{1}{4} + \frac{1}{6} = \frac{6}{24} + \frac{4}{24} = \frac{10}{24}$
   $\frac{10}{24} \times \frac{1}{2} = \frac{5}{24}$ which is not $\frac{1}{5}$
3. $\frac{720}{860} = \frac{36}{43}$
4. 13 sweets
5. 28 students

Page 16 – Decimals

Multiple-choice questions
1. b
2. c

3. c
4. b
5. d

Short-answer questions
1. a) True
   b) True
   c) True
2. a) Molly
   b) 1.201 seconds
   c) 0.002 seconds
3. a) 16
   b) 100
   c) 2000
   d) 0.1
   e) 24
   f) 0.01

GCSE-style questions
1. a) 6.14, 6.141, 7.208, 7.29, 7.42
   b) 1.28
   c) 34.199
   d) i) 7.21
      ii) 6.14
2. a) $\frac{629}{1000}$
   b) 0.28
3. a) Ryan: £3.40
      Dom: £2.03
   b) The total is £5.43. Ryan has added 3 and 4 together to get the 70 pence. He has also not written the money to 2 decimal places.
4. £104.88
5. a) 0.01
   b) 0.1
   c) 0.001

Page 18 – Percentages 1

Multiple-choice questions
1. c
2. c
3. d
4. d
5. a

Short-answer questions
1. 10% of 30 → 16
   5% of 15 → 3
   40% of 40 → 5
   25% of 20 → 0.75
2. 40%
3. £26 265
4. £1.80
5. 77%
6. £102

GCSE-style questions
1. £339.15
2. £29.90
3. £30.63
4. £4307.55
5. £85.50

Page 20 – Percentages 2

Multiple-choice questions
1. a
2. a
3. b

Short-answer questions
1. £7920
2. £391.51
3. £120 960
4. 115.5p
5. £168.03
6. £75.60

GCSE-style questions
1. £160
2. 1.61m
3. £42.92
4. £1000
5. a) 3.5%
   b) £757.12
6. £3400

Page 22 – Fractions, decimals & percentages

Multiple-choice questions
1. c
2. b
3. d
4. d
5. a

Short-answer questions
1.

Fraction	Decimal	Percentage
$\frac{2}{5}$	0.4	40%
$\frac{1}{20}$	0.05	5%
$\frac{1}{3}$	$0.\dot{3}$	$33.\dot{3}\%$
$\frac{1}{25}$	0.04	4%
$\frac{1}{4}$	0.25	25%
$\frac{1}{8}$	0.125	12.5%

2. 30%, $\frac{1}{3}$, 0.37, $\frac{3}{8}$, $\frac{1}{2}$, 0.62, 92%
3. Rosebushes is cheaper because $\frac{1}{4}$ = 25%, which is greater than the reduction at Gardens Are Us.

GCSE-style questions
1. $\frac{1}{8}$, 25%, 0.27, $\frac{1}{3}$, $\frac{2}{5}$, 0.571, 72%
2. Both will give the same answer because increasing by 20% is the same as multiplying by 1.2. Finding 10% then doubling it gives 20%, which when you add it to 40 is the same as increasing £40 by 20%.
3. She should choose Sheila's Bargains since the TV costs £217.38. The TV is £14.62 cheaper than the most expensive TV at Gita's TV Shop.

Page 24 – Approximations & using a calculator

Multiple-choice questions
1. d
2. b
3. d
4. c
5. c

Short-answer questions
1. a) True
   b) False
   c) False
   d) True
2. 8900m

3. a) 365
   b) 10.2
   c) 6320
4. a) 100
   b) 90
5. £120

GCSE-style questions
1. a) -856.859 65
   b) -857
2. 7.09
3. £210
4. a) 5.937 102 5
   b) $\frac{30 \times 6}{40 - 10} = \frac{180}{30} = 6$
5. a) 30 and 80
   b) 2400
   c) 49
6. $\frac{5}{2}$

Page 26 – Ratio

Multiple-choice questions
1. c
2. d
3. c
4. d
5. b

Short-answer questions
1. a) 1 : 3
   b) 1 : 4
   c) 1 : 3
2. 1176ml
3. a) £10.25
   b) 48g
4. £25 000
5. 4.5 days
6. €275

GCSE-style questions
1. £10.14
2. 6 days
3. The 1-litre bottle gives the better value for money: 25cl × 4 = 1 litre, so the cost of four 25cl bottles would be £1.56, while the 1-litre bottle costs £1.52.
4. a) $1237.50
   b) 164.43
5. Vicky: £6400
   Tracy: £8000
6. Butter: 125g
   Sugar: 100g
   Eggs: 5
   Flour: 112.5g
   Milk: 37.5ml

Page 28 – Indices

Multiple-choice questions
1. a
2. b
3. d
4. d
5. a

Short-answer questions
1. a) 64
   b) 32
   c) 81
   d) 64
2. a) False
   b) False
   c) True
   d) True
   e) False
   f) True

3. a) $6a^2$
   b) $3m^2$
   c) $20a^3b^5$
   d) n^{16}
   e) a^{12}
   f) $\frac{3}{4a^3}$
   g) $12a^{11}$
   h) $3b^2$
4. a) $n = 6$
   b) $n = 14$
   c) $n = 1$

GCSE-style questions
1. a) i) 16
      ii) 27
   b) 9^5
2. a) p^7
   b) n^4
   c) a^6
   d) $4ab$
   e) $9a^2$
3. a) 3
   b) 25
   c) 648
4. a) i) 8
      ii) 36
      iii) 32
   b) 5^4
   c) $3^4 = 81$
5. a) $6a^5$
   b) $3a$
   c) $\frac{1}{4b^2}$
6. a) i) 49
      ii) 243
      iii) 16
   b) 3^8

Algebra

Page 30 – Algebra

Multiple-choice questions
1. c
2. d
3. a
4. c
5. d

Short-answer questions
1. a) True
   b) True
   c) False
2. a) $3n - 9$
   b) $5(n + 3)$
   c) $n^2 + 3n$
   d) $8(n + 2)$
3. a) $5(2n + 3)$
   b) $12(2 - 3n)$
   c) $5(1 + 2n)$
   d) $4(5 - n)$
   e) $6a(a + 2)$

GCSE-style questions
1.

× 4 – 2	
Input	Output
1	2
2	6
4	14
6	22
9	34

2. a) $2t$
   b) $3y^2$
3. a) $6n$
   b) $6ab$
4. a) $4x + 4$
   b) i) $6(a + 2)$
      ii) $5a(2a - 3b)$
5. $n(n + 2) - 3(n - 1)$
   $= n^2 + 2n - 3n + 3$
   $= n^2 - n + 3$
6. a) $2(3a - 1) - (a - 2)$
      $= 6a - 2 - a + 2$
      $= 5a$
   b) i) $3(n - 4)$
      ii) $4p(2q - 3)$

Page 32 – Equations 1

Multiple-choice questions
1. c
2. a
3. d
4. b
5. c

Short-answer questions
1. a) $n = 9$
   b) $n = 2$
   c) $n = 2$
   d) $n = -7$
   e) $n = 18$
   f) $n = 1$
2. 1
3. a) $n = 5$
   b) $n = 3$
   c) $n = 7$
   d) $n = -5.5$
   e) $n = 25$
   f) $n = 4$
4. a) $n = 3$
   b) $n = 5$
   c) $n = 4$
   d) $n = 14$

GCSE-style questions
1. a) $n = 4$
   b) $n = 3$
   c) $n = 5$
   d) $n = 14$
2. a) $m = 3$
   b) $p = \frac{6}{10}$ or $p = \frac{3}{5}$
   c) $x = 6$
   d) $x = 6$
3. $x = \frac{9}{5} = 1\frac{4}{5}$
4. 6
5. $x = 1$

Page 34 – Equations 2 & inequalities

Multiple-choice questions
1. c
2. c
3. c
4. d
5. c

Short-answer questions
1. $2n + (n + 30°) + (n - 10°) = 180°$
   $4n + 20° = 180°$
   $n = 40°$
2. a) $x < 2$
   b) $x \geqslant 6$
   c) $1 \leqslant x \leqslant 4$
   d) $\frac{1}{3} \leqslant x \leqslant 2$
3. $t = 5.6$ or $t = -3.6$

GCSE-style questions
1. $x = 3$; shortest side = 8cm
2. a) -3, -2, -1, 0, 1, 2
   b) $p \leqslant 2$
3. $x = 2.7$ (You must show the full trial and improvement method in order to get full marks.)
4. $x = 2.8$ (You must show the full trial and improvement method in order to get full marks.)

Page 36 – Number patterns & sequences

Multiple-choice questions
1. d
2. a
3. c
4. b

Short-answer questions
1. a) 10, 12
   b) 16, 19
   c) 47, 57
   d) 0.75, 0.375
2. a) Even numbers
   b) Powers of 10
   c) Cube numbers
3. a) 22
   b) $3n + 4$
4. a) False
   b) False

GCSE-style questions
1. a)
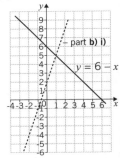

   b)

Pattern number	5	6
Number of dots	26	30

   c) 54
2. a) 13, 15
   b) Add 2 to the preceding term.
3. a) 2, 1, $\frac{1}{2}$
   b) $5n - 3$
4. $4n - 1$
5. Charlotte is not correct. The nth term of the sequence is $2n + 1$. $2n - 1$ is for the sequence 1, 3, 5, 7, ...

Page 38 – Formulae

Multiple-choice questions
1. d
2. c
3. b
4. c
5. a

Short-answer questions
1. True
2. a) 4
   b) $\frac{5}{4}$ or 1.25
   c) ±8
3. a) $b = \frac{p + 4}{3}$
   b) $b = \frac{4y + 6}{a}$
   c) $b = \frac{2 - 5n}{3}$

4. $T = 6b + 0.67m$ or $T = 600b + 67m$

GCSE-style questions
1. $p = 5n - 6$
2. a) £44.00
   b) £9.25
3. $C = 4w + 5b$
4. a) £153.90
   b) 31 hours
5. Peter's BMI $= \frac{89.5}{1.84^2} = 26.4$
   Peter would be classed as overweight.

Page 40 – Straight-line graphs & coordinates

Multiple-choice questions
1. b
2. d
3. a
4. b
5. d

Short-answer questions
1. 4
2. a) i)

x	-2	-1	0	1	2
$y = 6 - x$	8	7	6	5	4

   ii) See grid below.
   b) i)
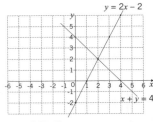

   ii) Gradient = 3
   c) (1, 5)

GCSE-style questions
1. a) Gradient = -1
   b)

   c) (2, 2)
2. a)

x	-2	-1	1	1	2
y	-7	-5	-3	-1	1

b)
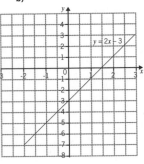

Page 42 – Curved graphs

Multiple-choice questions
1. b
2. d
3. c
4. d
5. b

Short-answer questions
1. a)

x	-2	-1	0	1	2	3
$y = x^2 - 2x - 2$	6	1	-2	-3	-2	1

   b)
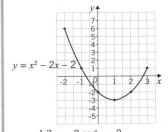

   c) i) $x = 0$ and $x = 2$
      ii) $x = 2.7$ and $x = -0.7$ (approximately)

GCSE-style questions
1. a)

x	-2	-1	0	1	2	3
$y = x^2 + 4$	8	5	4	5	8	13

   b)
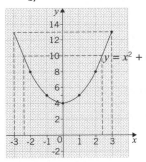

   c) i) $x = \pm 2.4$
      ii) $x = \pm 3$
2. a)

x	-2	-1	0	1	2
$y = x^3 + 1$	-7	0	1	2	9

   b)

Page 44 – Interpreting graphs

Multiple-choice questions
1. c
2. d
3. a
4. d

Short-answer questions
1. Vase A matches graph 2.
   Vase B matches graph 1.
   Vase C matches graph 3.
2. Statement 1 matches graph C.
   Statement 2 matches graph B.
   Statement 3 matches graph A.

GCSE-style questions
1. a) $C = 30h + 40$
   b) i) £100
      ii) £190
   c) Mrs. Robinson is correct. Since the standing charge is £40 and at £30 per hour $30 \times 8 = 240 + 40 = £280$.

Geometry and measures

Page 46 – Shapes

Multiple-choice questions
1. d
2. c
3. a
4. b
5. d

Short-answer questions
1. a) True
   b) False
   c) False
   d) False
   e) True
2. a) Eight
   b) 6

GCSE-style questions
1.
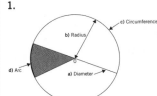

2. a) Quadrilateral
   b) Octagon
   c) Pentagon
   d) Triangle

3.

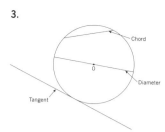

Page 48 – Solids

Multiple-choice questions
1. c
2. b
3. c
4. a
5. c

Short-answer questions
1. a) Cuboid
   b) Triangular prism
   c) Cylinder

2.

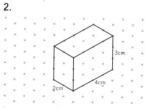

3. A, B and E

GCSE-style questions
1. a) Triangular prism
   b) Cylinder
2. Here is one possible answer:

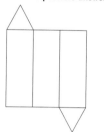

3.
a) Plan

b) Front elevation

c) Side elevation

Page 50 – Symmetry & constructions

Multiple-choice questions
1. a
2. c
3. a
4. c
5. b

Short-answer questions
1. a)

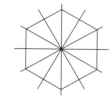

b)

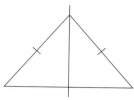

2. a)

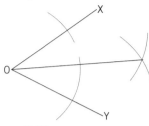

b) 50°

3. Your diagram should be drawn to scale:

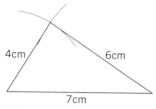

4cm   6cm
7cm

GCSE-style questions
1. a)

b) Order 2

2.

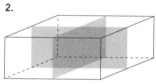

3. a)

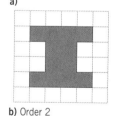

b) Order 2

4.

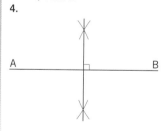

A ————————— B

Page 52 – Loci & coordinates in 3D

Multiple-choice questions
1. d
2. a
3. d
4. b

Short-answer questions
1.

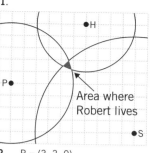

●H

P●

Area where Robert lives

●S

2. R = (3, 3, 0)
   S = (3, 1, 3)
   T = (0, 1, 3)
   U = (0, 1, 1)

GCSE-style questions
1.

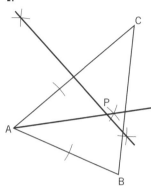

2.

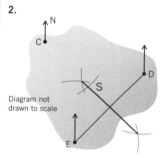

Diagram not drawn to scale

Page 54 – Angles

Multiple-choice questions
1. d
2. b
3. b
4. c
5. a

Short-answer questions
1. a) $n = 65°$
   b) $n = 63°$
   c) $n = 148°$
   d) $n = 68°$
   e) $n = 91°$
   f) $n = 60°$
   g) $n = 154°$
2. Here is one possible answer:

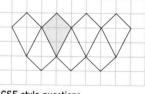

GCSE-style questions
1. $y = 40°$
2. a) i) $x = 18°$
      ii) If AB is vertical and BD is horizontal, ABE = 90°.
          So, angle x must be 18°.

b) i) $y = 54°$
   ii) Triangle BCD is isosceles, so angles BDC and BCD are equal. Hence y must be 54°.
c) i) $z = 54°$
   ii) Angle z is an alternate angle with angle BDC since CF and BE are parallel.

3. Sum of interior angles in a hexagon = $(2n - 4) × 90°$. Sum of angles in a hexagon is 720°. Angle $x = 105°$

Page 56 – Bearings & scale drawings

Multiple-choice questions
1. c
2. a
3. d
4. b

Short-answer questions
1. 10km
2. a) Your diagram should be drawn to scale:

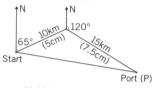

b) 11.1cm = 22.2km
c) 098° (±1°)
3. False, it is 240°.

GCSE-style questions
1. a) i) 310m
      ii) 060°
      iii)120°
   b)

2. Lengths of 4.5cm, 6cm and 7cm must be ±2mm.

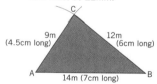

9m (4.5cm long)   12m (6cm long)
A   14m (7cm long)   B

Page 58 – Transformations 1

Multiple-choice questions
1. c
2. d
3. d
4. b

Short-answer questions
1. a)–c)

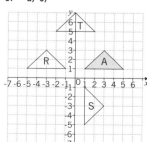

2. a) True
   b) True
   c) False
   d) True

GCSE-style questions

1. a) Reflection in the x-axis
   b) Rotation 90° anticlockwise about (0, 0)

2. a)–b)

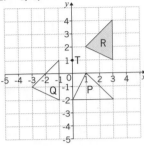

Page 60 – Transformations 2

Multiple-choice questions

1. d
2. b
3. b

Short-answer questions

1.

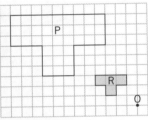

2. a) Reflection in the y-axis
   b) Rotation 90° clockwise about (0, 0)
   c) Reflection in the line $y = x$

GCSE-style questions

1. a)

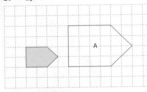

   b) 20cm²

2.

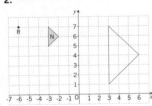

Page 62 – Measures & measurement 1

Multiple-choice questions

1. b
2. a
3. d
4. d
5. a

Short-answer questions

1.

12-hr	24-hr
4.23pm	**1623**
3.34pm	1534
9.26pm	2126
3.16pm	**1516**
3.14am	0314
9.38pm	**2138**

2. a) 7–10m
   b) About 240km
   c) 5ml

3. a)

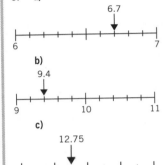

   b)

   c)

   d)

GCSE-style questions

1. a) i) 31 minutes
     ii) 14 minutes
   b) 1806
2. 1.73m
3. a) 19.6
   b) 20
   c)

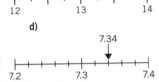

   d)

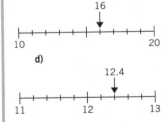

Page 64 – Measures & measurement 2

Multiple-choice questions

1. b
2. d
3. a
4. a
5. c

Short-answer questions

1. a) 8000m
   b) 3.25kg
   c) 7000kg
   d) 0.52m
   e) 2700ml
   f) 0.002 62km
2. 12.5 miles
3. 1.32 pounds
4. Lower limit = 46.5m
   Upper limit = 47.5m

---

5. 53.$\dot{3}$mph or $53\frac{1}{3}$mph
6. 0.1g/cm³

GCSE-style questions

1. a) 17.6 pounds
   b) 48km
2. 80kg
3. a) 1 hour 36 minutes = 96 minutes
   b) 4.$\dot{4}$km/h
4. Length = 12.05cm
   Width = 5.5cm
5. $S = \dfrac{2400}{108}$

$S = 22.\dot{2}$m/s

1m/s $= \dfrac{10}{4.47}$

Speed $= \dfrac{10}{4.47} \times 22.\dot{2}$

Speed = 49.7mph. Hence not speeding.

Page 66 – Pythagoras' theorem

Multiple choice questions

1. c
2. d
3. b
4. a

Short-answer questions

1. a) $n = 15$cm
   b) $n = 12.6$cm
   c) $n = 29.1$cm
   d) $n = 24.6$cm
2. Since
   $12^2 + 5^2 = 13^2$
   $144 + 25 = 169$
   the triangle must be right-angled for Pythagoras' theorem to be applied.
3. Both statements are true.
   Length of line $= \sqrt{6^2 + 3^2} = \sqrt{45} = 6.7$ (1 d.p.)
   Midpoint $= \left(\dfrac{2+5}{2}\right), \left(\dfrac{5+11}{2}\right)$
   = (3.5, 8)

GCSE-style questions

1. 13.7m
2. 6.4
3. 48.6m
4. £13.52

Page 68 – Area of 2D shapes

Multiple-choice questions

1. c
2. b
3. b
4. d
5. d

Short-answer questions

1. a) False
   b) True
   c) False
2. 85cm²
3. 38.6cm

GCSE-style questions

1. £33
2. £2170
3. 64cm (nearest cm)
4. 388.50m

Page 70 – Volume of 3D shapes

Multiple-choice questions

1. a
2. c
3. a
4. d

Short-answer questions

1. 1150cm³
2. Emily is not correct. The correct volume is 384 ÷ 2 = 192m³
3. 170.2m³
4. 9.9cm

GCSE-style questions

1. a) 288cm²
   b) 240cm³
2. 64cm³
3. a) 672cm³
   b) 0.000 672m³
4. £16.90
5. 1128cm³

Statistics and probability

Page 72 – Collecting data

Multiple-choice questions

1. b
2. d
3. a
4. b

Short-answer questions

1.

Type of book	Tally	Frequency

2. The tick boxes overlap. Which box would somebody who did 2 hours of homework tick?
The survey also needs to allow for students who do more than 4 hours of homework.
How much time do you spend doing homework each night?

0 up to 1 hour	1 up to 2 hours	2 up to 3 hours	3 up to 4 hours	4 hours or more

3. She is asking only men and not both men and women. She is also asking men who are interested in football as they are going to a football match, so her results will be biased.

GCSE-style questions

1.

Make of vehicle	Tally	Frequency

2. a) A good answer would be:
From the list below, tick your favourite chocolate bar.
Mars ☐
Twix ☐
Toblerone ☐
Galaxy ☐
Bounty ☐
Snickers ☐
Other
_____

2. b) This may not be a suitable sample since she is only asking one year group – she needs to get a representative sample across all ages. Secondly, 20 students is not really a sufficient number of students in the sample.

3. **The key to this question is to break it into subgroups.**
   • On average, how many hours per school day do you watch television?

   0 up to 1 hour ☐
   1 up to 2 hours ☐
   2 up to 3 hours ☐
   3 up to 4 hours ☐
   More than 4 hours ☐

   • On average, how many hours at the weekend do you watch television?

   0 up to 2 hours ☐
   2 up to 4 hours ☐
   4 up to 6 hours ☐
   6 up to 8 hours ☐
   More than 8 hours ☐

Page 74 – Representing data

Multiple-choice questions
1. d
2. c
3. a
4. b

Short-answer questions
1.

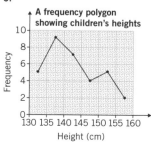

Salt and vinegar 150°
Beef
105°
Cheese and onion
15°
Smoky bacon

2.

Day	1	2	3	4	5	6	7
Hours of sunshine	3	4	1.5	1	1	3	1.5

GCSE-style questions
1. a) Thursday
   b) Wednesday
   c) 32
   d) Jackie is not correct. She sells 73 packets of cheese flavour crisps, whereas she sells 76 packets of salt 'n' vinegar crisps.
2. a) 390
   b) 390 + (150 × 10p) + (270 × 50p) + (90 × 20p) + (180 × 5p)
   Total = £567
3.

A frequency polygon showing children's heights

(graph: Frequency vs Height (cm), points at 130, 135, 140, 145, 150, 155, 160)

Page 76 – Scatter graphs & correlation

Multiple-choice questions
1. c
2. a
3. b

Short-answer questions
1. a) Positive correlation
   b) Negative correlation
   c) Positive correlation
   d) No or zero correlation
2. a) Positive correlation
   b)

(scatter graph: Physics (%) vs Mathematics (%) with Line of best fit)

   c) Approximately 72%

GCSE-style questions
1. a)

(scatter graph: Number of hours of sleep vs Age (in years) with Line of best fit)

   b) Negative correlation – the younger the child, the more hours of sleep they needed.
   c) See line of best fit on diagram above.
   d) A 4-year-old child has approximately 14 hours of sleep.
   e) This only gives an estimate as it follows the trend of the data. Similarly, if you continued the line it would assume that you may eventually need no hours of sleep at a certain age, which is not the case.
   f) The child psychologist is not correct. From the data, 5-year-old children have approximately 13 hours of sleep.

Page 78 – Averages 1

Multiple-choice questions
1. c
2. b
3. d

Short-answer questions
1. a) False
   b) True
   c) False
   d) True

2. a) 141.35 beans
   b) The manufacturer is justified in making this claim because the mean is just over 141, and the mode and median are also approximately 141.
3. x = 17

GCSE-style questions
1. a) 11.5
   b) 8
   c) 10.6
2. 7, 7, 13
3. 4.65
4. 81
5. £440

Page 80 – Averages 2

Multiple-choice questions
1. c
2. b
3. a
4. a

Short-answer questions
1. 21.5mm
2. a) 47
   b) 35
   c) 40

GCSE-style questions
1.
   1 | 2 4 9 5 7 8 8 5
   2 | 2 7 3 5 7 7
   3 | 1 6 5 2 8
   4 | 1

   Reordering gives:
   1 | 2 4 5 5 7 8 8 9
   2 | 2 3 5 7 7 7
   3 | 1 2 5 6 8
   4 | 1
   Key: 1 | 2 = 12 minutes

2. a) £31.80
   b) This is only an estimate because the midpoints of the data have been used.
   c) $30 \leqslant x < 40$
   d) Although the modal class interval is $10 \leqslant x < 20$, since the mean is £31.80 and the median class interval is $30 \leqslant x < 40$, Edward's claim is not correct because the other averages indicate that the average amount spent is between £30 and £40.

Page 82 – Probability 1

Multiple-choice questions
1. c
2. d
3. c
4. b
5. a

Short-answer questions
1. a) $\frac{2}{11}$
   b) $\frac{2}{11}$
   c) $\frac{3}{11}$
   d) 0
2. 0.4
3. a) True
   b) False
   c) False
4. 100 students

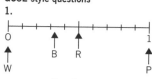
(number line with O, W, B, R, P, 1)

2. a) i) $\frac{5}{20} = \frac{1}{4}$
      ii) $\frac{7}{20}$
   b) $\frac{16}{20} = \frac{4}{5}$
3. a) i) 0.35
      ii) 0
   b) There cannot be 12 counters in the bag because 0.1 × 12 = 1.2, hence not a whole number of white counters.
   c) 50 times

Page 84 – Probability 2

Multiple-choice questions
1. c
2. a
3. a
4. d

Short-answer questions
1. a)

	1	2	3	3
1	2	3	4	4
2	3	4	5	5
3	4	5	6	6
6	7	8	9	9

   b) i) $\frac{4}{16} = \frac{1}{4}$
      ii) $\frac{2}{16} = \frac{1}{8}$
      iii) 0
2. HO, HT, CO, CT, BO, BT
   (H = Ham; C = Cheese; B = Beef; O = Orange juice; T = Tea)

GCSE-style questions
1. a) $\frac{6}{36} = \frac{1}{6}$
   b) $\frac{4}{36} = \frac{1}{9}$
2. a)

	Under 13 years old	13 years and over	Total
Boys	15	**27**	42
Girls	**12**	21	**33**
Total	**27**	**48**	75

   b) $\frac{27}{75} = \frac{9}{25}$
3. SS, SF, TS, TF, AS, AF
4. £25

Answers

6

Published by Letts Educational Ltd.
An imprint of HarperCollins*Publishers*

Text © Fiona Mapp
Design and illustration © Letts Educational Ltd.

GCSE-style questions

Answer all parts of the questions. Show your workings (on a separate sheet of paper if necessary) and include the correct units in your answers.

1 Write down the mathematical name of each of these 3D shapes.

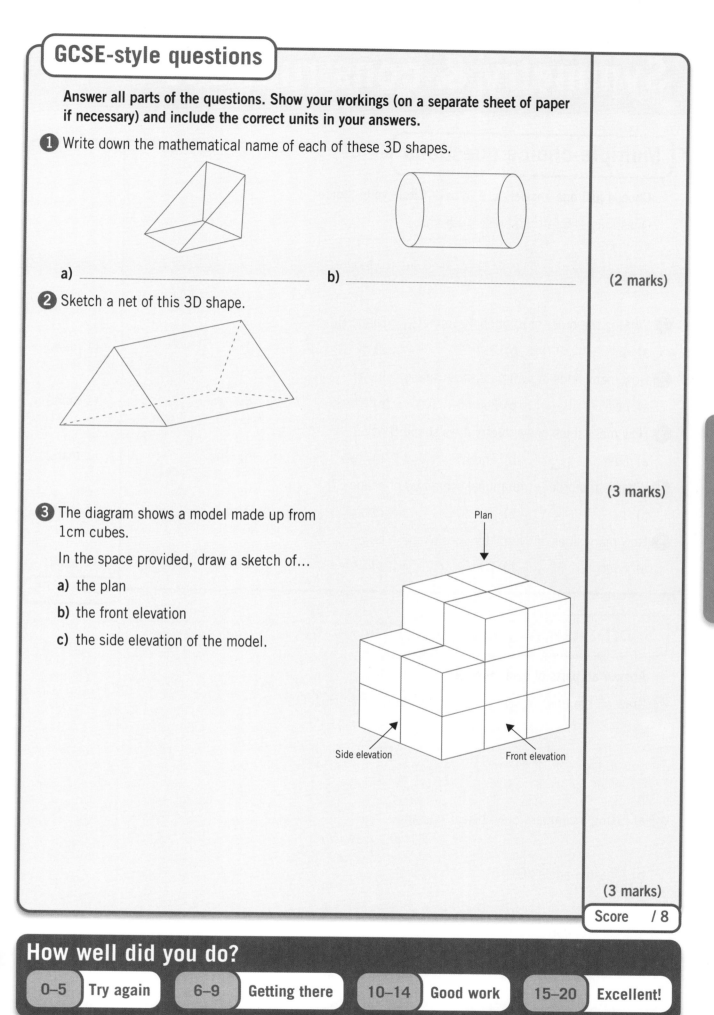

a) .... b) .... **(2 marks)**

2 Sketch a net of this 3D shape.

(3 marks)

3 The diagram shows a model made up from 1cm cubes.

In the space provided, draw a sketch of...

a) the plan

b) the front elevation

c) the side elevation of the model.

Plan

Side elevation   Front elevation

(3 marks)

Score   / 8

How well did you do?

| 0–5 | Try again | 6–9 | Getting there | 10–14 | Good work | 15–20 | Excellent! |

For more information on this topic, see pages 50–51 of your Success Revision Guide.

Symmetry & constructions

Multiple-choice questions

Choose just one answer, a, b, c or d. Circle your choice.

Questions 1–5 refer to these diagrams.

A   B C   D

❶ What is the order of rotational symmetry of shape B?

a) 4   **b)** 2   **c)** 3   **d)** 1   (1 mark)

❷ How many lines of symmetry does shape D have?

a) Five   **b)** Four   **c)** Three   **d)** Two   (1 mark)

❸ How many lines of symmetry does shape B have?

a) Four   **b)** Three   **c)** Two   **d)** One   (1 mark)

❹ What is the order of rotational symmetry of shape C?

a) 1   **b)** 3   **c)** 2   **d)** 4   (1 mark)

❺ How many lines of symmetry does shape A have?

a) Four   **b)** Two   **c)** Three   **d)** One   (1 mark)

Score   / 5

Short-answer questions

Answer all parts of each question.

❶ Draw all the lines of symmetry on each of the shapes below.

a)

b)

(4 marks)

❷ **a)** Using a compass only, bisect this angle.

(2 marks)

b) Measure angle XOY.

_____

(1 mark)

❸ On a separate piece of paper, using a ruler and a compass only, make an accurate drawing of this triangle.

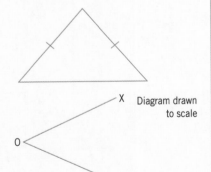

Diagram drawn to scale

Diagram not accurately drawn

4cm

6cm

7cm

(3 marks)

Score   / 10

50

Answer all parts of the questions. Show your workings (on a separate sheet of paper if necessary) and include the correct units in your answers.

1 a) Draw the line(s) of symmetry on the rectangle below.

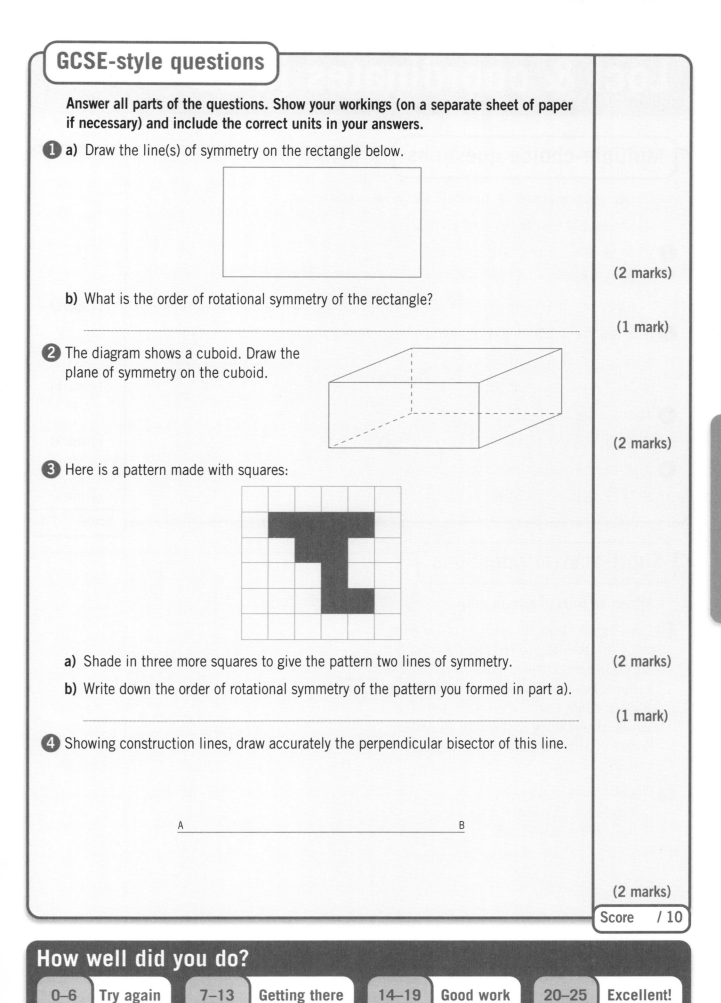

(2 marks)

b) What is the order of rotational symmetry of the rectangle?

_____

(1 mark)

2 The diagram shows a cuboid. Draw the plane of symmetry on the cuboid.

(2 marks)

3 Here is a pattern made with squares:

a) Shade in three more squares to give the pattern two lines of symmetry.

(2 marks)

b) Write down the order of rotational symmetry of the pattern you formed in part a).

_____

(1 mark)

4 Showing construction lines, draw accurately the perpendicular bisector of this line.

A   B

(2 marks)

Score   / 10

How well did you do?

| 0–6 | Try again | 7–13 | Getting there | 14–19 | Good work | 20–25 | Excellent! |

For more information on this topic, see pages 52–54 of your Success Revision Guide.

Loci & coordinates in 3D

Multiple-choice questions

Choose just one answer, a, b, c or d. Circle your choice.

Questions 1–4 refer to the diagram opposite.

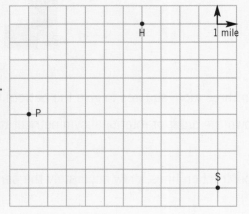

1 What are the coordinates of point A?

   a) (4, 3, 1)   **b)** (4, 3, 0)

   c) (0, 3, 1)   **d)** (4, 0, 1)   **(1 mark)**

2 What are the coordinates of point B?

   a) (0, 3, 1)   **b)** (0, 0, 0)

   c) (4, 3, 0)   **d)** (0, 3, 0)   **(1 mark)**

3 What are the coordinates of point C?

   a) (0, 3, 1)   **b)** (4, 3, 1)   **c)** (4, 0, 0)   **d)** (4, 3, 0)   **(1 mark)**

4 What are the coordinates of point D?

   a) (4, 3, 0)   **b)** (4, 3, 1)   **c)** (0, 0, 0)   **d)** (0, 3, 0)   **(1 mark)**

Score   / 4

Short-answer questions

Answer all parts of each question.

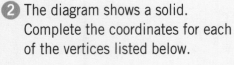

1 The diagram shows the position of the post office (P), the hospital (H) and the school (S). Robert lives less than 4 miles away from the hospital, less than 5 miles away from the post office and less than 8 miles away from the school. Use shading to show the area where Robert lives. Use a scale of 1 grid square = 1 mile.

                           (4 marks)

2 The diagram shows a solid. Complete the coordinates for each of the vertices listed below.

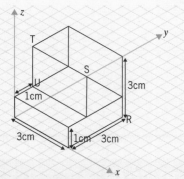

   R = (_____, _____, _____)

   S = (_____, _____, _____)

   T = (_____, _____, _____)

   U = (_____, _____, _____)

                           (4 marks)

Score   / 8

GCSE-style questions

Answer all parts of the questions. Show your workings (on a separate sheet of paper if necessary) and include the correct units in your answers.

1 In this question you should use a ruler and a compass only for the constructions.

Triangle ABC is the plan of an adventure playground.

P is an ice-cream kiosk inside the adventure playground.
P is the same distance from A as it is from C.
P is the same distance from AC as it is from AB.

On the diagram, clearly mark the point P.

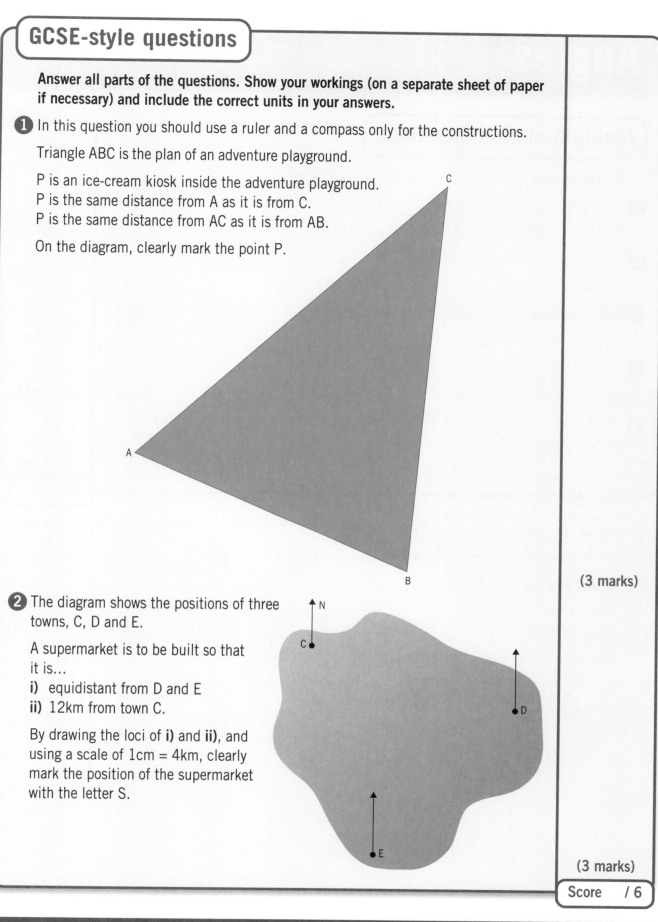

(3 marks)

2 The diagram shows the positions of three towns, C, D and E.

A supermarket is to be built so that it is...
i) equidistant from D and E
ii) 12km from town C.

By drawing the loci of **i)** and **ii)**, and using a scale of 1cm = 4km, clearly mark the position of the supermarket with the letter S.

(3 marks)

Score   / 6

How well did you do?

0–4 **Try again**   5–9 **Getting there**   10–14 **Good work**   15–18 **Excellent!**

For more information on this topic, see page 55 of your Success Revision Guide.

Angles

Multiple-choice questions

Choose just one answer, a, b, c or d. Circle your choice.

1 What is the size of a right angle?

   a) 72°   **b)** 360°   **c)** 180°   **d)** 90°

                                                   (1 mark)

2 In the diagram opposite, what is the size of angle a?

   a) 90°   **b)** 80°   **c)** 75°   **d)** 100°   (1 mark)

(Diagram: quadrilateral with angles 105°, 110°, 65° and a)

3 Two angles in a scalene triangle are 104° and 39°. What is the size of the third angle?

   a) 217°   **b)** 37°   **c)** 57°   **d)** 157°   (1 mark)

4 When shapes tessellate, what is the total of the angles at the point at which they meet?

   a) 180°   **b)** 90°   **c)** 360°   **d)** 270°   (1 mark)

5 The size of the exterior angle of a regular polygon is 20°. How many sides does the polygon have?

   a) 18   **b)** 15   **c)** 10   **d)** 20   (1 mark)

Score   / 5

Short-answer questions

Answer all parts of each question.

1 Here are the sizes of some angles, written on cards.

   148°   60°   91°   63°   154°   65°   68°

Match the correct card to the missing angle n in each of the diagrams.

a)

$n = $ _____

b)

$n = $ _____

c)

$n = $ _____

d)

$n = $ _____

e)

$n = $ _____

f)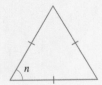

$n = $ _____

g)

$n = $ _____

                                   (7 marks)

2 On the grid, draw six more shapes to continue this tessellation.

                                   (2 marks)

Score   / 9

GCSE-style questions

Answer all parts of the questions. Show your workings (on a separate sheet of paper if necessary) and include the correct units in your answers.

1. Find the size of the angle marked y. You must show all your working.

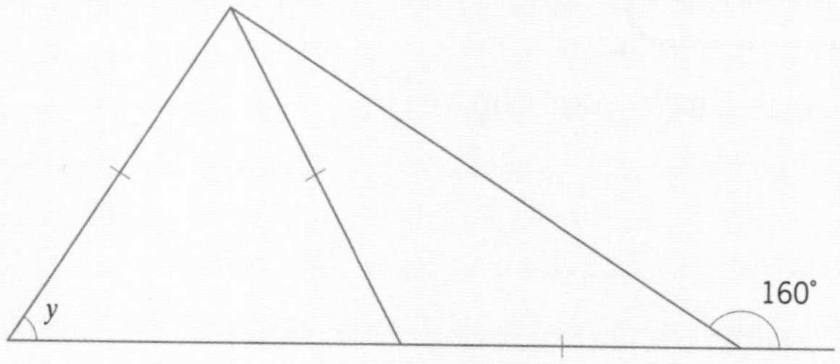

y
160°

.... ° **(4 marks)**

2. In the diagram, AB is a vertical straight line and BDE is a horizontal straight line. BC = BD, CF is parallel to BDE.

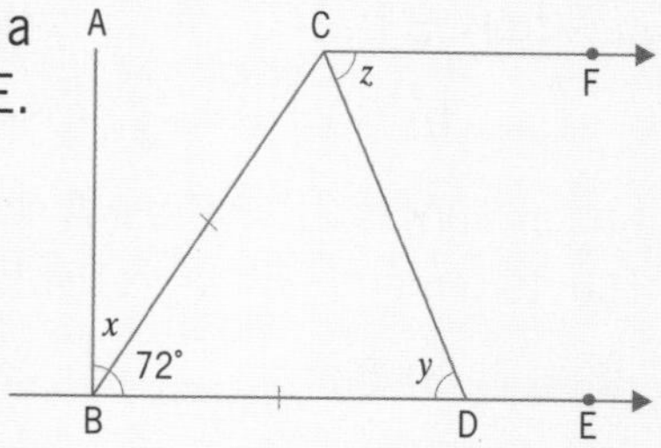

A
C
z
F
x
72°
y
B
D
E

a) i) Work out the size of the angle marked x.

.... ° **(2 marks)**

ii) Give a reason for your answer.

....

.... **(2 marks)**

b) i) Work out the size of the angle marked y. .... ° **(2 marks)**

ii) Give a reason for your answer.

....

.... **(2 marks)**

c) i) Work out the size of the angle marked z. .... ° **(2 marks)**

ii) Give a reason for your answer.

....

.... **(2 marks)**

3. The diagram shows a hexagon.
Find the size of the angle marked $x°$.

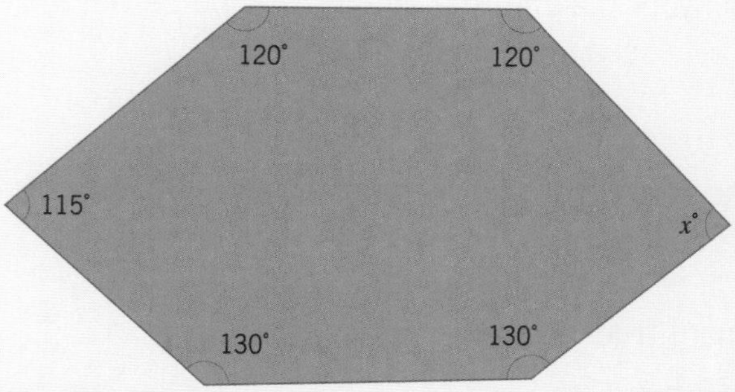

120°
120°
115°
x°
130°
130°

....

....

.... ° **(4 marks)**

Score / 20

How well did you do?

0–8	Try again	9–16	Getting there	17–26	Good work	27–34	Excellent!

For more information on this topic, see pages 49 and 56–57 of your Success Revision Guide.

Bearings & scale drawings

Multiple-choice questions

Choose just one answer, a, b, c or d. Circle your choice.

1 The bearing of P from Q is 050°. What is the bearing of Q from P?

 a) 130°   **b)** 50°   **c)** 230°   **d)** 310°   (1 mark)

2 The bearing of R from S is 130°. What is the bearing of S from R?

 a) 310°   **b)** 230°   **c)** 050°   **d)** 200°   (1 mark)

3 The bearing of A from B is 240°. What is the bearing of B from A?

 a) 120°   **b)** 60°   **c)** 320°   **d)** 060°   (1 mark)

4 The length of a car park is 25 metres. A scale diagram of the car park is being drawn to a scale of 1cm to 5 metres. What is the length of the car park on the scale diagram?

 a) 500mm   **b)** 5cm   **c)** 50cm   **d)** 5m   (1 mark)

Score   / 4

Short-answer questions

Answer all parts of each question.

1 The scale on a road map is 1 : 50 000. Two towns are 20cm apart on the map. Work out the real distance, in km, between the two towns.

_____ km   (2 marks)

2 A ship sails on a bearing of 065° for 10km. It then continues on a bearing of 120° for a further 15km to a port (P).

 a) On a separate piece of paper, draw, using a scale of 1cm to 2km, an accurate scale drawing of this information.   (3 marks)

 b) Measure on your diagram the direct distance between the starting point and port P.

 _____ km   (1 mark)

 c) What is the bearing of port P from the starting point?

 _____ °   (1 mark)

3 Is this statement **true** or **false**?

 'The bearing of B from A is 060°.'

 _____   (1 mark)

Score   / 8

56

GCSE-style questions

Answer all parts of the questions. Show your workings (on a separate sheet of paper if necessary) and include the correct units in your answers.

1 The scale drawing shows the positions of points A, B, C and D.
Point C is due east of point A.

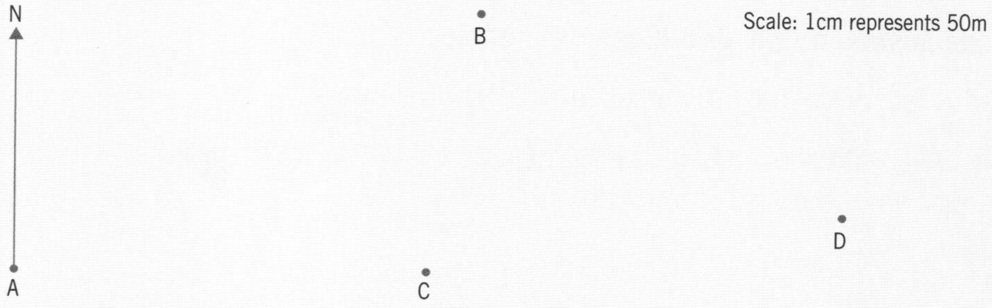

N
B
D
A
C
Scale: 1cm represents 50m

a) Use measurements from the drawing to find...

i) the distance, in metres, of B from A ………………… m **(1 mark)**

ii) the bearing of B from A ………………… ° **(2 marks)**

iii) the bearing of D from B. ………………… ° **(2 marks)**

b) Point E is 250m from point C on a bearing of 055°.
Mark the position of point E on the diagram above. **(2 marks)**

2 Here is a sketch of a triangle. Use a compass and a ruler to make an accurate scale drawing of the triangle. Use a scale of 1cm to 2m. The line AB has been drawn for you below.

Diagram not accurately drawn

C
9m
12m
A
14m
B

A
B
14m

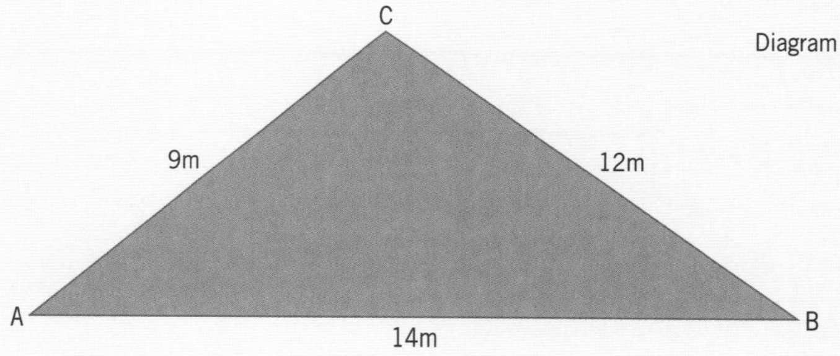

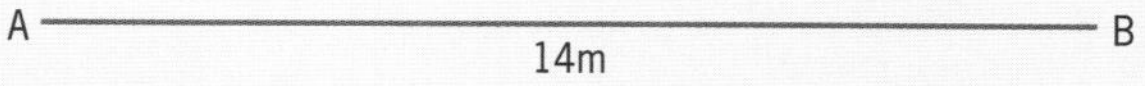

(3 marks)

Score / 10

How well did you do?

0–5	Try again	6–10	Getting there	11–17	Good work	18–22	Excellent!

For more information on this topic, see pages 58–59 of your Success Revision Guide.

Transformations 1

Multiple-choice questions

Choose just one answer, a, b, c or d. Circle your choice.

Questions 1–4 refer to the diagram opposite.

1 Shape A is mapped onto shape B by a reflection.
What is the equation of the line of reflection?

a) $y = 1$ **b)** $x = 2$
c) $y = x$ **d)** $y = -x$ (1 mark)

2 Shape A is mapped onto shape C by a translation.
What is the vector of translation?

a) $\binom{3}{7}$ **b)** $\binom{-7}{3}$
c) $\binom{7}{3}$ **d)** $\binom{-3}{-7}$ (1 mark)

3 Shape A is mapped onto shape D by a rotation. Through what angle is it rotated?

a) $110°$ **b)** $55°$ **c)** $180°$ **d)** $90°$ (1 mark)

4 What special name is given to the relationship between triangles A, B, C and D?

a) Enlargement   **b)** Congruent   **c)** Translation   **d)** Similar   (1 mark)

Score   / 4

Short-answer questions

Answer all parts of each question.

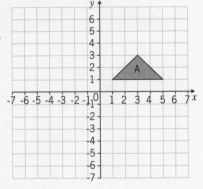

1 On the grid, carry out the following transformations.

a) Reflect shape A in the y-axis.
Call the new shape R.

b) Rotate shape A 90° clockwise, about (0, 0).
Call the new shape S.

c) Translate shape A by the vector $\binom{-3}{4}$.
Call the new shape T.   (3 marks)

2 State whether the following statements are **true** or **false**.

a) Shape P can be transformed
to shape A by a translation. _____ (1 mark)

b) Shape P can be transformed
to shape B by a rotation. _____ (1 mark)

c) Shape P can be transformed
to shape C by a reflection. _____ (1 mark)

d) Shape P can be transformed
to shape D by a reflection. _____ (4 marks)

Score   / 7

Answer all parts of the questions. Show your workings (on a separate sheet of paper if necessary) and include the correct units in your answers.

1

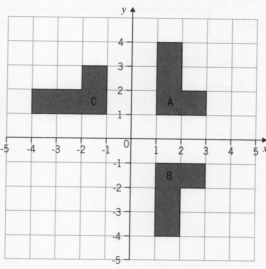

a) Describe fully the single transformation that takes shape A onto shape B.

....

....

(2 marks)

b) Describe fully the single transformation that takes shape A onto shape C.

....

....

(3 marks)

2

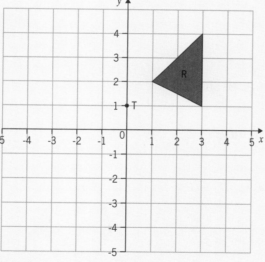

The triangle R has been drawn on the grid.

a) Rotate triangle R 90° clockwise about the point T (0, 1) and call the image P.   (3 marks)

b) Translate triangle R by the vector $\binom{-4}{-3}$ and call the image Q.   (3 marks)

Score   / 11

Geometry and measures

How well did you do?

0–6 | Try again   7–10 | Getting there   11–16 | Good work   17–22 | Excellent!

Transformations 2

Multiple-choice questions

Choose just one answer, a, b, c or d. Circle your choice.

Questions 1–3 refer to the diagram opposite.

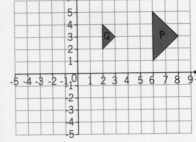

1 Shape P is enlarged to give shape Q.
What is the scale factor of the enlargement?

   a) $\frac{1}{3}$ **b)** 2   **c)** 3   **d)** $\frac{1}{2}$ (1 mark)

2 Shape Q is enlarged to give shape P.
What is the scale factor of the enlargement?

   a) $\frac{1}{3}$ **b)** 2   **c)** 3   **d)** $\frac{1}{2}$ (1 mark)

3 What are the coordinates of the centre of enlargement?

   a) (3, -2)   **b)** (-2, 3)   **c)** (-3, 4)   **d)** (0, 0)   (1 mark)

Score   / 3

Short-answer questions

Answer all parts of each question.

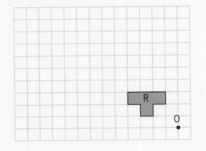

1 Draw an enlargement of shape R, with centre O and scale factor 3. Call the image P.

(3 marks)

2 The diagram shows the position of three shapes, A, B and C.

  a) Describe the transformation that moves A onto C.

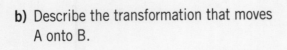

(2 marks)

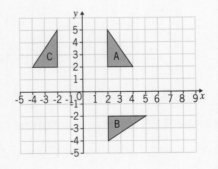

  b) Describe the transformation that moves A onto B.

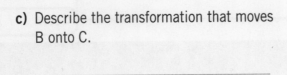

(2 marks)

  c) Describe the transformation that moves B onto C.

_____

_____

(2 marks)

Score   / 9

60

Answer all parts of the questions. Show your workings (on a separate sheet of paper if necessary) and include the correct units in your answers.

1 a) Draw an enlargement of the shape below.
Use a scale factor of 2.
Call the enlarged shape A.

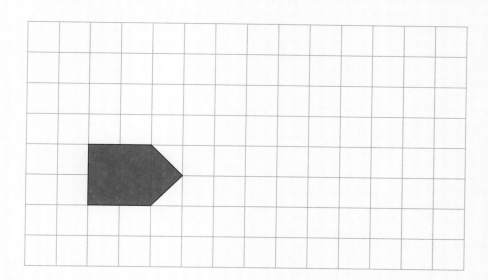

(2 marks)

b) If the area of the original shape is 5cm^2, what is the area of the enlarged shape?

_____ cm^2

(1 mark)

2 Enlarge triangle N by a scale factor of 3 with centre R (-6, 7).

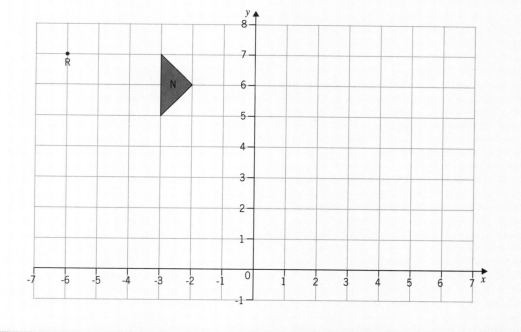

(3 marks)

Score   / 6

Geometry and measures

How well did you do?

| 0–3 | Try again | 4–8 | Getting there | 9–13 | Good work | 14–18 | Excellent! |

For more information on this topic, see pages 62–63 of your Success Revision Guide.

Measures & measurement 1

Multiple-choice questions

Choose just one answer, a, b, c or d. Circle your choice.

1 Approximately how many kilograms would an 'average' man weigh?

   a) 720kg   **b)** 72kg   **c)** 7.2kg   **d)** 45kg   (1 mark)

2 How many seconds are in three minutes?

   a) 180   **b)** 60   **c)** 240   **d)** 120   (1 mark)

3 What is 1842 written in 12-hour time?

   a) 6.42am   **b)** 6.15am   **c)** 6.42   **d)** 6.42pm   (1 mark)

4 What is 5.25am written in 24-hour time?

   a) 5.25pm   **b)** 0525am   **c)** 0525pm   **d)** 0525   (1 mark)

5 How many days are there in a leap year?

   a) 366   **b)** 364   **c)** 365   **d)** 367   (1 mark)

Score   / 5

Short-answer questions

Answer all parts of each question.

1 Complete the table below with the correct times.

12-hour clock	4.23pm	....	....	3.16pm	....	9.38pm
24-hour clock	....	1534	2126	....	0314	....

(2 marks)

2 Using metric units, estimate…

   a) the length of your classroom   ....   (1 mark)

   b) the distance from Manchester to London   ....   (1 mark)

   c) the volume of medicine on a medicine spoon.   ....   (1 mark)

3 On the scales below, mark the following readings with an arrow (↓).

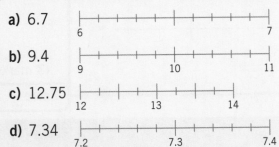

   a) 6.7   (1 mark)

   b) 9.4   (1 mark)

   c) 12.75   (1 mark)

   d) 7.34   (1 mark)

Score   / 9

GCSE-style questions

Answer all parts of the questions. Show your workings (on a separate sheet of paper if necessary) and include the correct units in your answers.

1 Part of a train timetable is shown.

Manchester	1415		1521	
Stafford	1503		1612	
Milton Keynes	1555	1605	1701	1715
Watford		1638		1748
Euston	1646	1701	1752	1806

Sarah travels from Stafford to Watford. She has to change trains at Milton Keynes.

a) i) Sarah arrives in Stafford at 1541 to catch the next train. How long does she have to wait in Stafford for the next train?

.... minutes (1 mark)

ii) How long does Sarah have to wait at Milton Keynes for the next train to Watford?

.... minutes (2 marks)

b) Briony is travelling from Milton Keynes to Euston. She arrives at Milton Keynes at 1710. What time does she arrive in Euston?

.... (1 mark)

2 Daniel's height is 1.67 metres. Rachel is 6 centimetres taller than Daniel. Work out Rachel's height. Give your answer in metres.

.... m (2 marks)

3 a) Write down the reading marked with an arrow on this meter.

.... (1 mark)

b) Write down the reading marked with an arrow on this scale.

.... (1 mark)

c) Find the number 16 on the number line. Mark it with an arrow ($\downarrow$).

10   20 (1 mark)

d) Find the number 12.4 on the number line. Mark it with an arrow ($\downarrow$).

11   12   13 (1 mark)

Score   / 10

Geometry and measures

How well did you do?

| 0–6 | Try again | 7–12 | Getting there | 13–18 | Good work | 19–24 | Excellent! |

For more information on this topic, see pages 64–67 of your Success Revision Guide.

63

Measures & measurement 2

Multiple-choice questions

Choose just one answer, a, b, c or d. Circle your choice.

1 What is 2500g in kilograms?

   a) 25kg   **b)** 2.5kg   **c)** 0.25kg   **d)** 250kg   **(1 mark)**

2 Approximately how many pounds are in 4kg?

   a) 6.9   **b)** 12.4   **c)** 7.7   **d)** 8.8   **(1 mark)**

3 Jessica is 165cm tall to the nearest cm. What is the lower limit of her height?

   a) 164.5cm   **b)** 165.5cm   **c)** 165cm   **d)** 164.9cm   **(1 mark)**

4 What is the speed of a train if it travels 60km in 30 minutes?

   a) 120km/h   **b)** 0.75km/h   **c)** 75km/h   **d)** 80km/h   **(1 mark)**

5 A car travels for $2\frac{1}{2}$ hours at a speed of 42mph. How far does the car travel? 🖩

   a) 96 miles   **b)** 100 miles   **c)** 105 miles   **d)** 140 miles   **(1 mark)**

Score   / 5

Short-answer questions

Answer all parts of each question.

1 Complete the statements below.

   a) 8km = _____ m   **b)** 3250g = _____ kg

   c) 7 tonnes = _____ kg   **d)** 52cm = _____ m

   e) 2.7 litres = _____ ml   **f)** 262cm = _____ km   **(6 marks)**

2 Two towns are approximately 20km apart. How many miles is this? 🖩

   (1 mark)

3 A recipe uses 600g of flour. Approximately how many pounds is this? 🖩

   (1 mark)

4 A field is 47 metres long to the nearest metre. Write down the upper and lower limits of the length of the field. 🖩

   (2 marks)

5 Giovanni drove 200 miles in 3 hours and 45 minutes. At what average speed did he travel? 🖩

   (2 marks)

6 What is the density of a toy if its mass is 200g and its volume is 2000cm³?

   (2 marks)

Score   / 14

Answer all parts of the questions. Show your workings (on a separate sheet of paper if necessary) and include the correct units in your answers.

1 a) Change 8 kilograms into pounds. 🔲

_____ pounds   (2 marks)

b) Change 30 miles into kilometres.

_____ km   (2 marks)

2 Two solids each have a volume of 2.5m³.
The density of solid A is 320kg per m³.
The density of solid B is 288kg per m³.

Calculate the difference in the masses of the solids. 🔲 _____ kg   (3 marks)

3 Amy took part in a sponsored walk. She walked from the school to the park and back. The distance from the school to the park is 8km.

a) Amy walked from the school to the park at an average speed of 5km/h. Find the time she took to walk from the school to the park. 🔲

_____ minutes   (2 marks)

b) Her average speed for the return journey was 4km/h. Calculate her average speed for the whole journey. 🔲

_____ km/h   (4 marks)

4 The length of this rectangle is 12.1cm to the nearest mm. The width of the rectangle is 6cm to the nearest cm. Write down the lower limits for the length and width of the rectangle.

12.1cm

6cm

Length _____ cm

Width _____ cm   (2 marks)

5 The speed limit through some roadworks is 50mph. Cameras recorded the time taken for a car to travel 2400m through the roadworks as 108 seconds. 10mph is approximately 4.47m/s. Was the car speeding through the roadworks? You must show your working. 🔲

_____

_____   (5 marks)

Score   / 20

How well did you do?

0–15 Try again   16–23 Getting there   24–31 Good work   32–39 Excellent!

For more information on this topic, see pages 64–67 of your Success Revision Guide.

65

Pythagoras' theorem

Multiple-choice questions

Choose just one answer, a, b, c or d. Circle your choice.

1 Point A has coordinates (1, 4) and point B has coordinates (4, 10). What are the coordinates of the midpoint of the line AB?

a) (5, 14) **b)** (3, 6) **c)** (2.5, 7) **d)** (1.5, 3)   (1 mark)

2 Point C has coordinates (-3, 5) and point D has coordinates (5, 12). What are the coordinates of the midpoint of the line CD?

a) (1, 3.5) **b)** (4, 8.5) **c)** (4, 3.5) **d)** (1, 8.5)   (1 mark)

3 Calculate the missing length y of this triangle.

a) 169cm **b)** 13cm

c) 17cm **d)** 84.5cm   (1 mark)

4 Calculate the missing length y of this triangle.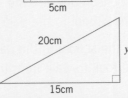

a) 13.2cm **b)** 5cm

c) 25cm **d)** 625cm   (1 mark)

Score   / 4

Short-answer questions

Answer all parts of each question.

1 Calculate the missing lengths of these right-angled triangles. Give your answer to 3 significant figures, where appropriate.

a)  **b)** **c)**  **d)**

$n =$ _____ cm $n =$ _____ cm $n =$ _____ cm $n =$ _____ cm   (8 marks)

2 Molly says, 'The angle $x°$ in this triangle is 90°.'
Explain how Molly knows this without measuring the size of the angle.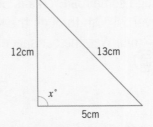

_____

_____   (2 marks)

3 Colin says, 'The length of this line is 6.7 units (1 d.p.). The coordinates of the midpoint are (3.5, 8).' Decide whether these statements are **true** or **false**. Give an explanation for your answer.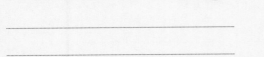

_____

_____   (2 marks)

Score   / 12

Answer all parts of the questions. Show your workings (on a separate sheet of paper if necessary) and include the correct units in your answers.

1 Calculate the perpendicular height of this isosceles triangle.
Give your answer to 1 decimal place. 🖩

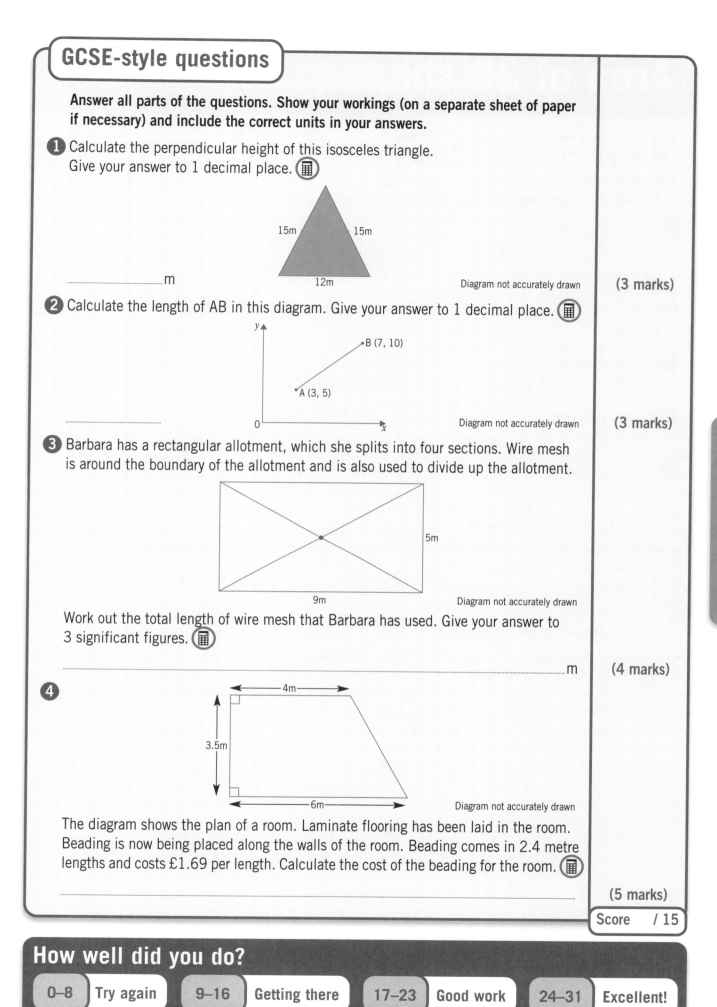

................................m   Diagram not accurately drawn   **(3 marks)**

2 Calculate the length of AB in this diagram. Give your answer to 1 decimal place. 🖩

....   Diagram not accurately drawn   **(3 marks)**

3 Barbara has a rectangular allotment, which she splits into four sections. Wire mesh is around the boundary of the allotment and is also used to divide up the allotment.

Diagram not accurately drawn

Work out the total length of wire mesh that Barbara has used. Give your answer to 3 significant figures. 🖩

................................m   **(4 marks)**

4

Diagram not accurately drawn

The diagram shows the plan of a room. Laminate flooring has been laid in the room. Beading is now being placed along the walls of the room. Beading comes in 2.4 metre lengths and costs £1.69 per length. Calculate the cost of the beading for the room. 🖩

....   **(5 marks)**

Score   / 15

Geometry and measures

How well did you do?

| 0–8 | Try again | 9–16 | Getting there | 17–23 | Good work | 24–31 | Excellent! |

For more information on this topic, see pages 68–69 of your Success Revision Guide.

Area of 2D shapes

Multiple-choice questions

Choose just one answer, a, b, c or d. Circle your choice.

1 What is the area of this triangle?

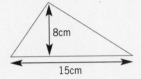

a) 60mm²   b) 120cm²

c) 60cm²   d) 46cm²

(1 mark)

2 If the area of a rectangle is 20cm² and its width is 2.5cm, what is its length?

a) 9cm   b) 8cm   c) 7.5cm   d) 2.5cm

(1 mark)

3 Change 50 000cm² into m².

a) 500m²   b) 5m²   c) 0.5m²   d) 50m²

(1 mark)

4 What is the approximate circumference of a circle of radius 4cm?

a) 25.1cm²   b) 50.3cm   c) 12.6cm   d) 25.1cm

(1 mark)

5 What is the area of this circle? Use π = 3.14.

a) 25.1cm²   b) 55cm²

c) 12.6cm²   d) 50.24cm²

(1 mark)

Score   / 5

Short-answer questions

Answer all parts of each question.

1 For each of the diagrams below, state whether the area given is **true** or **false**.

a)
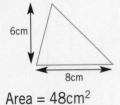

Area = 48cm²

b)
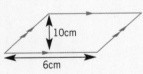

Area = 60cm²

c)
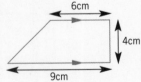

Area = 108cm²

(3 marks)

2 Calculate the area of the green shaded region.

_____ cm²

(3 marks)

3 Calculate the perimeter of this shape, correct to 1 decimal place.

_____ cm

(3 marks)

Score   / 9

GCSE-style questions

Answer all parts of the questions. Show your workings (on a separate sheet of paper if necessary) and include the correct units in your answers.

1 The diagram opposite shows the plan of a garden. Lawn seed is to be sown to cover the garden. Lawn seed comes in 500g packets and covers 14m². A packet of lawn seed costs £5.50. Work out the total cost of the lawn seed needed.

Diagram not accurately drawn

15m

8m

5m

9m

_____

_____

_____

_____

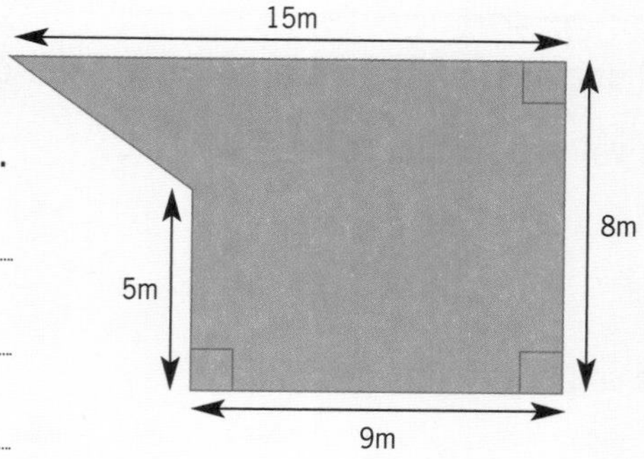

(5 marks)

2 The diagram opposite shows the plan of a room. Underfloor heating is being installed in the room. 1m² of underfloor heating costs £155. Work out the total cost of installing underfloor heating for the whole room.

Diagram not accurately drawn

3m

3.5m

5m

_____

_____

_____

_____

_____

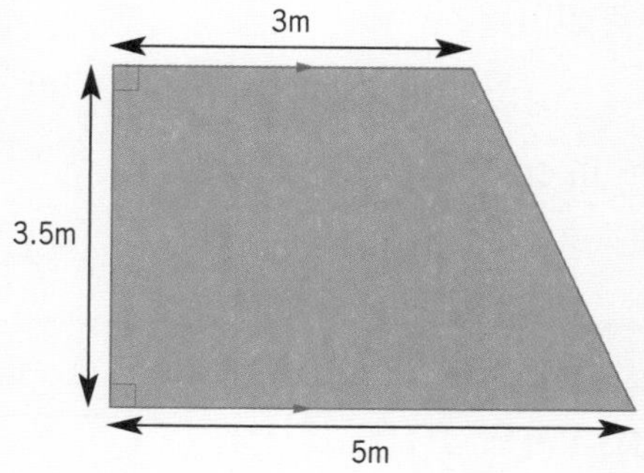

(5 marks)

3 The circumference of a circle is 200cm. Calculate the diameter of the circle. Give your answer correct to the nearest centimetre. 🖩

_____

_____ **cm** **(3 marks)**

4 The diagram opposite shows the plan of a running track. Work out the total distance of the running track. Give your answer to 2 decimal places. 🖩

Diagram not accurately drawn

60m

Track →

100m

_____

_____

_____

_____

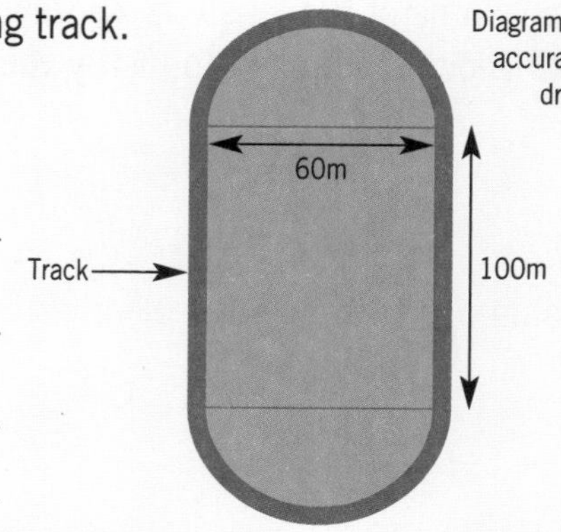

(3 marks)

Score   / 16

How well did you do?

| 0–8 | Try again | 9–14 | Getting there | 15–22 | Good work | 23–30 | Excellent! |

For more information on this topic, see pages 70–71 of your Success Revision Guide.

69

Volume of 3D shapes

Multiple-choice questions

Choose just one answer, a, b, c or d. Circle your choice.

1 What is the volume of this cuboid?

   a) 30cm³   **b)** 16cm³

   c) 300mm³   **d)** 15cm³   **(1 mark)**

(cuboid labelled 2cm, 3cm, 5cm)

2 What is the volume of this prism?

   a) 64cm³   **b)** 240cm³

   c) 120cm³   **d)** 20cm³   **(1 mark)**

(prism labelled 4cm, 10cm, 6cm)

3 The volume of a cuboid is 20cm³. If its height is 1cm and its width is 4cm, what is its length?

   a) 5cm   **b)** 10cm   **c)** 15cm   **d)** 8cm   **(1 mark)**

4 What is 5m³ in cm³?

   a) 500cm³   **b)** 5000cm³   **c)** 500 000cm³   **d)** 5 000 000cm³   **(1 mark)**

Score   / 4

Short-answer questions

Answer all parts of each question.
Use the π key where appropriate.

1 The diagram shows a toy.
Work out its volume.

_____ cm³   **(3 marks)**

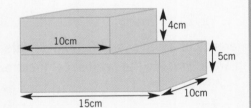

(labelled 4cm, 10cm, 5cm, 15cm, 10cm)

2 Emily says, 'The volume of this prism is 384m³.'
Is Emily correct? Show working out to justify your answer.

_____

_____   **(1 mark)**

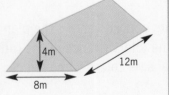

(labelled 4m, 12m, 8m)

3 Calculate the volume of this cylinder, clearly stating your units. 📱

_____

_____   **(2 marks)**

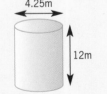

(labelled 4.25m, 12m)

4 If the volume of both these solids is the same, work out the height of the cylinder to 1 decimal place. 📱

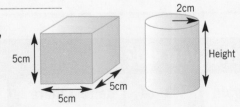

(labelled 5cm, 5cm, 5cm, 2cm, Height)

_____ cm   **(4 marks)**

Score   / 10

Answer all parts of the questions. Show your workings (on a separate sheet of paper if necessary) and include the correct units in your answers.

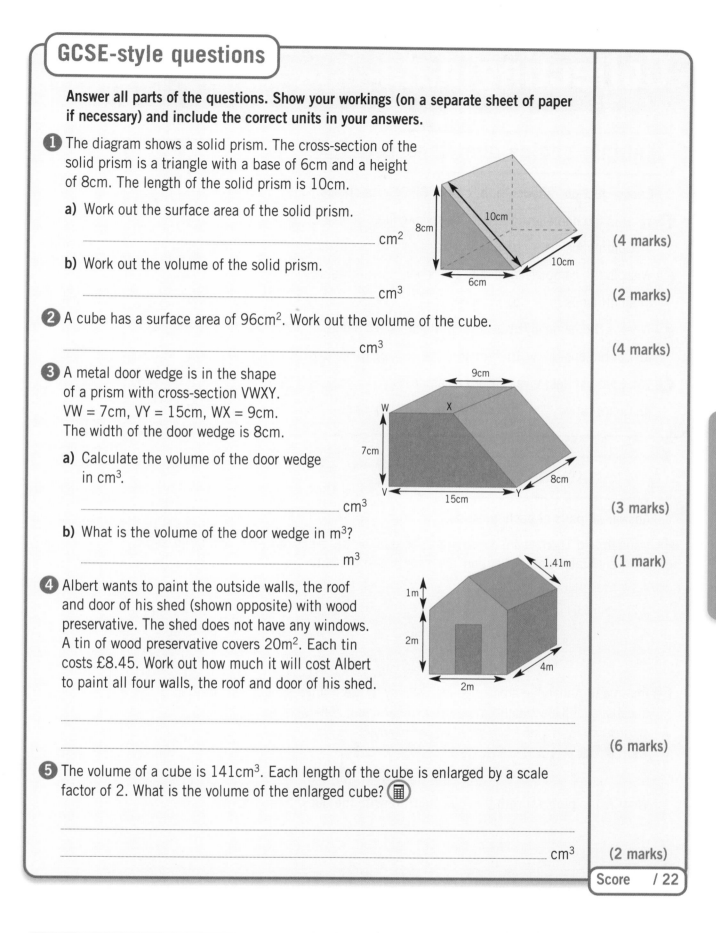

1 The diagram shows a solid prism. The cross-section of the solid prism is a triangle with a base of 6cm and a height of 8cm. The length of the solid prism is 10cm.

a) Work out the surface area of the solid prism.

_____ cm²   (4 marks)

b) Work out the volume of the solid prism.

_____ cm³   (2 marks)

2 A cube has a surface area of 96cm². Work out the volume of the cube.

_____ cm³   (4 marks)

3 A metal door wedge is in the shape of a prism with cross-section VWXY. VW = 7cm, VY = 15cm, WX = 9cm. The width of the door wedge is 8cm.

a) Calculate the volume of the door wedge in cm³.

_____ cm³   (3 marks)

b) What is the volume of the door wedge in m³?

_____ m³   (1 mark)

4 Albert wants to paint the outside walls, the roof and door of his shed (shown opposite) with wood preservative. The shed does not have any windows. A tin of wood preservative covers 20m². Each tin costs £8.45. Work out how much it will cost Albert to paint all four walls, the roof and door of his shed.

_____

_____   (6 marks)

5 The volume of a cube is 141cm³. Each length of the cube is enlarged by a scale factor of 2. What is the volume of the enlarged cube?

_____

_____ cm³   (2 marks)

Score   / 22

Geometry and measures

How well did you do?

| 0–9 | Try again | 10–19 | Getting there | 20–28 | Good work | 29–36 | Excellent! |

For more information on this topic, see pages 72–73 of your Success Revision Guide.

Collecting data

Multiple-choice questions

Choose just one answer, a, b, c or d. Circle your choice.

1 What is the name given to data that you collect yourself?

   a) Continuous   **b)** Primary   **c)** Secondary   **d)** Discrete   **(1 mark)**

2 What is the name given to data that takes specific values?

   a) Continuous   **b)** Primary   **c)** Secondary   **d)** Discrete   **(1 mark)**

3 What is the name given to data in which values merge from one category to the next?

   a) Continuous   **b)** Primary   **c)** Secondary   **d)** Discrete   **(1 mark)**

4 What type of data gives a word as an answer?

   a) Quantitative   **b)** Qualitative   **c)** Continuous   **d)** Discrete   **(1 mark)**

Score   / 4

Short-answer questions

Answer all parts of each question.

1 Hannah and Thomas are collecting some data on the types of books read by students. Draw a suitable data collection sheet for this information.

(3 marks)

2 Imran and Annabelle are designing a survey to use in their school. One of their questions is: 'How much time do you spend doing homework per night?'

0–1 hr	1–2 hrs	2–3 hrs	3–4 hrs

What is the problem with this question? Rewrite the question to improve it.

....

....

(2 marks)

3 Emily decides to carry out a survey on how much football people watch on television. She decides to ask 50 men outside a football ground on Saturday afternoon. Explain why her results will be biased.

....

....

(2 marks)

Score   / 7

Answer all parts of the questions. Show your workings (on a separate sheet of paper if necessary) and include the correct units in your answers.

1 Siân is going to carry out a survey to record information about the make of vehicles passing the school gate.

In the space below, draw a suitable data collection sheet that Siân could use.

(3 marks)

2 Mrs Robinson is going to sell chocolate bars at the school tuck shop. She wants to know what type of chocolate bars pupils like.

a) Design a suitable questionnaire she could use.

(2 marks)

b) Mrs Robinson decides to give the questionnaire to 20 students in year 7. Explain why this may not be a suitable sample.

(2 marks)

3 Iain is conducting a survey into the television habits of students at his school. One of the questions in his survey is: 'Do you watch a lot of television?'

His friend Daisy tells him that it is not a very good question. Write down two ways in which Iain could improve the question.

(2 marks)

Score   / 9

Statistics and probability

How well did you do?

| 0–4 | Try again | 5–8 | Getting there | 9–14 | Good work | 15–20 | Excellent! |

For more information on this topic, see pages 76–77 of your Success Revision Guide.

Representing data

Multiple-choice questions

Choose just one answer, a, b, c or d. Circle your choice.

For these questions, use the information shown in the frequency diagram (histogram).

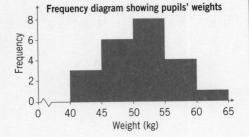

Frequency diagram showing pupils' weights

1 How many pupils had a weight between 50 and 55kg?

a) 4   b) 6
c) 10   d) 8   (1 mark)

2 How many pupils had a weight of less than 50kg?

a) 7   b) 8   c) 9   d) 10   (1 mark)

3 How many pupils had a weight of over 60kg?

a) 1   b) 2   c) 3   d) 4   (1 mark)

4 How many pupils took part in the survey?

a) 8   b) 22   c) 5   d) 20   (1 mark)

Score   / 4

Short-answer questions

Answer all parts of each question.

1 Sarah carried out a survey to find the favourite flavours of crisps of students in her class. Her results are shown in the table below.

Crisp flavour	Number of students
Cheese and onion	7
Salt and vinegar	10
Beef	6
Smoky bacon	1

Draw an accurate pie chart to show this information. 🖩   (4 marks)

2 The number of hours of sunshine during the first seven days in May are shown on the line graph. Use the information on the graph to complete the table.

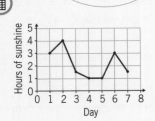

Day	1	2	3	4	5	6	7
Hours of sunshine	3		1.5	1	1		

(3 marks)

Score   / 7

74

Answer all parts of the questions. Show your workings (on a separate sheet of paper if necessary) and include the correct units in your answers.

1. Jackie works in a newsagents. One week she collects some data on the flavour of crisps her customers bought. Jackie makes a bar chart of her results.

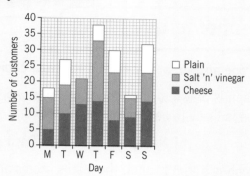

a) On which day was the highest number of packets of crisps sold? _____ (1 mark)

b) On which day were no plain flavour crisps sold? _____ (1 mark)

c) How many packets of crisps were sold on Sunday? _____ (1 mark)

d) Jackie says that she sells more cheese-flavour crisps. Decide whether Jackie is right, giving a reason for your answer.

_____ (3 marks)

2. A vending machine is emptied every day. The pie chart represents the number of each type of coin in the machine.

The machine contains 150 ten pence coins.

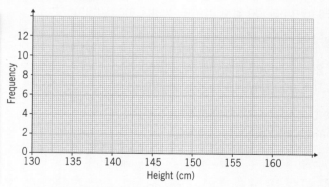

a) How many £1 coins are there? 📱

_____ (1 mark)

b) Calculate the total amount of money in the machine. 📱

_____ (4 marks)

3. The table shows the heights of children in a class.

Height (h) in cm	Frequency
$130 \leqslant h < 135$	5
$135 \leqslant h < 140$	9
$140 \leqslant h < 145$	7
$145 \leqslant h < 150$	4
$150 \leqslant h < 155$	5
$155 \leqslant h < 160$	2

Draw a frequency polygon for this data on the grid provided. (3 marks)

Score / 14

Statistics and probability

How well did you do?

| 0–6 | Try again | 7–10 | Getting there | 11–17 | Good work | 18–25 | Excellent! |

For more information on this topic, see pages 78–81 of your Success Revision Guide.

75

Scatter graphs & correlation

Multiple-choice questions

Choose just one answer, a, b, c or d. Circle your choice.

① A scatter graph is drawn to show the height and weight of some students. What type of correlation is likely to be shown?

   a) Zero   **b)** Negative   **c)** Positive   **d)** Scattered   **(1 mark)**

② A scatter graph is drawn to show the maths scores and waist measurements of a group of students. What type of correlation is likely to be shown?

   a) Zero   **b)** Negative   **c)** Positive   **d)** Scattered   **(1 mark)**

③ A scatter graph is drawn to show the age of some cars and their values. What type of correlation is likely to be shown?

   a) Zero   **b)** Negative   **c)** Positive   **d)** Scattered   **(1 mark)**

Score   / 3

Short-answer questions

Answer all parts of each question.

① Some statements have been written on cards:

(Positive correlation)   (Negative correlation)   (No correlation)

Decide which card best describes these relationships.

   a) The outside temperature and the sales of ice lollies   ....   **(1 mark)**

   b) The outside temperature and the sales of woollen gloves ....   **(1 mark)**

   c) The mass of a person and his/her waist measurement   ....   **(1 mark)**

   d) The height of a person and his/her IQ   ....   **(1 mark)**

② The scatter graph shows the marks scored in mathematics and physics examinations.

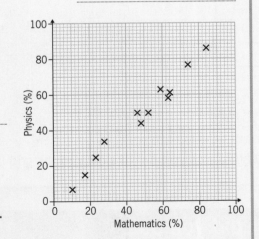

   a) Describe the relationship between the mathematics and physics scores.

   ....   **(1 mark)**

   b) Draw a line of best fit on the scatter graph.   **(1 mark)**

   c) Use your line of best fit to estimate the mathematics score that Jonathan is likely to obtain if he has a physics score of 75%.

   ....   **(1 mark)**

Score   / 7

Answer all parts of the questions. Show your workings (on a separate sheet of paper if necessary) and include the correct units in your answers.

1 The table shows the ages of some children and the total number of hours of sleep they had between noon on Saturday and noon on Sunday.

Age (years)	2	6	5	3	12	9	2	10	5	10	7	11	12	3
No. of hours of sleep	15	13.1	13.2	14.8	10.1	11.8	15.6	11.6	13.5	11.8	12.8	10.2	9.5	14

a) Plot the information from the table in the form of a scatter graph.

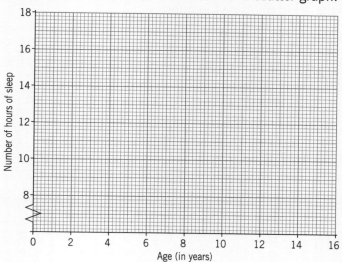

(4 marks)

b) Describe the correlation between the age of the children in years and the total number of hours of sleep they had.

_____

_____

(2 marks)

c) Draw a line of best fit on your diagram.

(1 mark)

d) Estimate the total number of hours of sleep for a 4-year-old child.

_____

(2 marks)

e) Explain why the line of best fit only gives an estimate for the number of hours slept.

_____

_____

(2 marks)

f) A child psychologist states, '5-year-old children have between 15 and 16 hours of sleep a night.' Decide, based on the data above, whether the child psychologist is correct.

_____

(1 mark)

Score   / 12

How well did you do?

| 0–5 | Try again | 6–11 | Getting there | 12–16 | Good work | 17–22 | Excellent! |

For more information on this topic, see pages 82–83 of your Success Revision Guide.

77

Averages 1

Multiple-choice questions

Choose just one answer, a, b, c or d. Circle your choice.

1 What is the mean of this set of data? 2, 7, 1, 4, 2, 6, 2, 5, 2, 6

   a) 4.2   **b)** 3.6   **c)** 3.7   **d)** 3.9   (1 mark)

2 What is the median value of the set of data used in question 1?

   a) 2   **b)** 3   **c)** 4   **d)** 5   (1 mark)

3 A dice is thrown and the scores are noted. The results are shown in the table below. What is the mean dice score? 🖩

Dice score	1	2	3	4	5	6
Frequency	12	15	10	8	14	13

   a) 5   **b)** 3   **c)** 4   **d)** 3.5   (1 mark)

Score / 3

Short-answer questions

Answer all parts of each question.

1 Here are some number cards:

8	7	11	4	2	1	3	12	4	4

State whether the following statements, which refer to the number cards above, are **true** or **false**.

   a) The range of the number cards is 1–11. .... (1 mark)

   b) The mean of the number cards is 5.6. .... (1 mark)

   c) The median of the number cards is 5. .... (1 mark)

   d) The mode of the number cards is 4. .... (1 mark)

2 A baked beans factory claims, 'On average, a tin of baked beans contains 141 beans.'

In order to check the accuracy of this claim, a sample of 20 tins was taken and the number of beans in each tin counted.

Number of beans	137	138	139	140	141	142	143	144
Number of tins	1	1	1	2	5	4	4	2

   a) Calculate the mean number of beans per tin. 🖩 .... (2 marks)

   b) Explain briefly whether you think the manufacturer is justified in making its claim.

.... (1 mark)

3 The mean of 7, 9, 10, 18, x and 17 is 13. What is the value of x? .... (2 marks)

Score / 9

Answer all parts of the questions. Show your workings (on a separate sheet of paper if necessary) and include the correct units in your answers.

1 Grace made a list of the ages of some children in her swimming club.

7, 8, 7, 14, 10, 12, 12, 7, 12, 12, 11, 15

  a) Find the median age of the children. _____ (2 marks)

  b) Find the range of the ages of the children. _____ (1 mark)

  c) Find the mean age of the children, correct to 1 decimal place.

_____ (3 marks)

2 Here are three hidden cards:

(?)   (?)   (?)

The mode of the three numbers is 7. The mean of the three numbers is 9.
What are the three numbers?

_____ (3 marks)

3 Some students took a test. The table gives information about their marks in the test.

Mark	Frequency
3	2
4	5
5	11
6	2

Work out the mean mark.

_____ (3 marks)

4 Simon has sat three examinations. His mean score is 65. To pass the unit, he needs to get an average of 69. What score must he get in the fourth and final examination to pass the unit?

_____

_____ (3 marks)

5 A company employs three women and seven men. The mean weekly wage of the ten employees is £464. The mean weekly wage of the three women is £520. Calculate the mean weekly wage of the seven men.

_____

_____ (4 marks)

Score   / 19

Statistics and probability

How well did you do?

| 0–10 | Try again | 11–16 | Getting there | 17–24 | Good work | 25–31 | Excellent! |

For more information on this topic, see pages 84–85 of your Success Revision Guide.

Averages 2

Multiple-choice questions

Choose just one answer, a, b, c or d. Circle your choice.

The following questions are based on the information given in the table opposite about the time taken in seconds to swim 50 metres.

Time t (seconds)	Frequency (f)
$0 \leqslant t < 30$	1
$30 \leqslant t < 60$	2
$60 \leqslant t < 90$	4
$90 \leqslant t < 120$	6
$120 \leqslant t < 150$	7
$150 \leqslant t < 180$	2

❶ How many people swam 50 metres in less than 60 seconds?

a) 2   **b)** 4
c) 3   **d)** 6

(1 mark)

❷ Which of the intervals is the modal class?

a) $60 \leqslant t < 90$ **b)** $120 \leqslant t < 150$ **c)** $30 \leqslant t < 60$ **d)** $90 \leqslant t < 120$

(1 mark)

❸ Which of the class intervals contains the median value?

a) $90 \leqslant t < 120$ **b)** $150 \leqslant t < 180$ **c)** $120 \leqslant t < 150$ **d)** $60 \leqslant t < 90$

(1 mark)

❹ What is an estimate for the mean time taken to swim 50 metres? 🖩

a) 105 seconds   **b)** 385 seconds   **c)** 100 seconds   **d)** 125 seconds

(1 mark)

Score   / 4

Short-answer questions

Answer all parts of each question.

❶ Information about the length of some seedlings is shown in the table opposite.

Calculate an estimate for the mean length of the seedlings. 🖩

Mean = _____ mm

Length L (mm)	Number of seedlings
$0 \leqslant L < 10$	3
$10 \leqslant L < 20$	5
$20 \leqslant L < 30$	9
$30 \leqslant L < 40$	2
$40 \leqslant L < 50$	1

(4 marks)

❷ The stem-and-leaf diagram shows the marks gained by some students in a mathematics examination.

Using the stem-and-leaf diagram, work out...

a) the mode _____

b) the median _____

c) the range. _____

```
1 | 2 5 7
2 | 6 9
3 | 4 5 5 7
4 | 2 7 7 7 7
5 | 2
```

Key: 1 | 2 = 12 marks

(1 mark)
(1 mark)
(1 mark)

Score   / 7

Answer all parts of the questions. Show your workings (on a separate sheet of paper if necessary) and include the correct units in your answers.

1 A psychologist records the times, to the nearest minute, taken by 20 students to complete a logic problem. Here are the results:

12	22	31	36	35	14	27	23	19	25
15	17	15	27	32	38	41	18	27	18

Draw an ordered stem-and-leaf diagram to show this information.

(4 marks)

2 Edward asks 100 people how much they spent last year on newspapers. The results are given in the table below.

Amount £ (x)	Frequency
$0 \leqslant x < 10$	12
$10 \leqslant x < 20$	20
$20 \leqslant x < 30$	15
$30 \leqslant x < 40$	18
$40 \leqslant x < 50$	14
$50 \leqslant x < 60$	18
$60 \leqslant x < 70$	3

a) Calculate an estimate of the mean amount spent on newspapers. 🖩

(4 marks)

b) Explain briefly why this value of the mean is only an estimate.

(1 mark)

c) Calculate the class interval in which the median lies.

(2 marks)

d) Edward claims, 'The average amount of money spent on newspapers last year was between £10 and £20.' Explain whether you think that Edward's claim is correct.

(2 marks)

Score   / 13

How well did you do?

| 0–6 | Try again | 7–11 | Getting there | 12–17 | Good work | 18–24 | Excellent! |

For more information on this topic, see pages 86–87 of your Success Revision Guide.

Probability 1

Multiple-choice questions

Choose just one answer, a, b, c or d. Circle your choice.

1 A bag of sweets contains five hard centres and three soft centres. What is the probability of choosing a hard centre if a sweet is picked out of the bag at random?

a) $\frac{3}{5}$ **b)** $\frac{3}{8}$ **c)** $\frac{5}{8}$ **d)** $\frac{1}{2}$ (1 mark)

2 The probability that Highbury football club wins a football match is $\frac{12}{17}$
What is the probability that the club does **not** win the football match?

a) $\frac{5}{12}$ **b)** $\frac{17}{29}$ **c)** $\frac{12}{17}$ **d)** $\frac{5}{17}$ (1 mark)

3 A fair dice is thrown 600 times. On how many of these throws would you expect to get a 4?

a) 40   **b)** 600   **c)** 100   **d)** 580   (1 mark)

4 A fair dice is thrown 500 times. If a 6 comes up 87 times, what is the relative frequency?

a) $\frac{1}{6}$ **b)** $\frac{87}{500}$ **c)** $\frac{10}{600}$ **d)** $\frac{1}{587}$ (1 mark)

5 The probability that it will rain tomorrow is 0.35
What is the probability that it will **not** rain tomorrow?

a) 0.65   **b)** 0.35   **c)** 0.25   **d)** 1.35   (1 mark)

Score   / 5

Short-answer questions

Answer all parts of each question.

1 The letters M A T H E M A T I C S are each placed on a separate piece of card and put into a bag. Stuart picks out a card at random. What is the probability that he picks the following cards?

a) The letter T   **b)** The letter M

c) The letters A or C   **d)** The letter R   (4 marks)

2 The probability that George wins a tennis match is 0.6
What is the probability that George does **not** win the tennis match?   (1 mark)

3 State whether each of these statements is **true** or **false**.

a) The probability of getting a 6 when a fair dice is thrown is $\frac{1}{6}$ (1 mark)

b) The probability of passing a test in physics is 0.3.
If 100 students sit the test, the number expected to pass would be 3.   (1 mark)

c) The probability that Conkers football team wins a match is 0.8.
The probability that the team will not win the match is 0.4.   (1 mark)

4 The probability of achieving a grade A in French is 0.2.
If 500 students sit the exam, how many students would you expect to achieve a grade A?

(2 marks)

Score   /10

Answer all parts of the questions. Show your workings (on a separate sheet of paper if necessary) and include the correct units in your answers.

1 A bag contains four blue, two green and six red counters. A counter is chosen at random from the bag.

On the probability scale above...

a) label with the letter R the probability of choosing a red counter (1 mark)

b) label with the letter B the probability of choosing a blue counter (1 mark)

c) label with the letter W the probability of choosing a white counter (1 mark)

d) label with the letter P the probability of choosing a blue, green or red counter. (1 mark)

2 There are 20 different-coloured sweets in a jar. The colour of each sweet is red, green, yellow or blue. The table shows how many sweets of each colour are in the jar.

Colour	Red	Green	Yellow	Blue
Number	4	5	7	4

Reece picks one sweet at random from the jar.

a) Write down the probability that he will pick...

i) a green sweet _____ ii) a yellow sweet. _____ (2 marks)

b) Write down the probability that he will not pick a blue sweet. _____ (2 marks)

3 A bag contains different beads of four different colours – red, white, blue and pink. The table shows the probability of taking a bead of a particular colour at random.

Colour	Red	White	Blue	Pink
Probability	0.25	0.1		0.3

Mary is going to take a bead at random and then put it back in the bag.

a) i) Work out the probability that Mary will take out a blue bead. _____ (2 marks)

ii) Write down the probability that Mary will take out a black bead. _____ (1 mark)

b) Mary says there are exactly 12 counters in the bag. Mary is wrong. Explain why there cannot be exactly 12 counters in the bag.

_____ (1 mark)

c) Mary will take out a bead from the bag at random 200 times, replacing the bead each time. Work out an estimate for the number of times that Mary will take a red bead.

_____ (2 marks)

Score / 14

How well did you do?

| 0–6 | Try again | 7–13 | Getting there | 14–22 | Good work | 23–29 | Excellent! |

For more information on this topic, see pages 88–89 of your *Success Revision Guide*.

Probability 2

Multiple-choice questions

Choose just one answer, a, b, c or d. Circle your choice.

1 Two fair dice are thrown and their scores are added. What is the probability of a score of 5?

a) $\frac{1}{2}$ b) $\frac{2}{12}$ c) $\frac{4}{36}$ d) $\frac{5}{36}$ (1 mark)

2 Two fair dice are thrown and their scores are multiplied. What is the probability of a score of 1?

a) $\frac{1}{36}$ b) $\frac{1}{12}$ c) $\frac{2}{12}$ d) $\frac{2}{36}$ (1 mark)

3 The probability that it snows on Christmas Day is 0.2
What is the probability that it will **not** snow on Christmas Day?

a) 0.8 b) 0.4 c) 0.16 d) 0.04 (1 mark)

4 The probability that Fiona is in the hockey team is 0.7
What is the probability that Fiona is **not** in the hockey team?

a) 1.7 b) 9.3 c) 0.7 d) 0.3 (1 mark)

Score   / 4

Short-answer questions

Answer all parts of each question.

Spinner 1: 3 3 / 2 1

Spinner 2: 6 2 / 3 1

1 Two spinners are spun at the same time and their scores are added.

a) Complete the sample space diagram to show the possible outcomes.

Spinner 1

		1	2	3	3
Spinner 2	1	2			
	2			5	
	3		5		
	6		8	9	

(2 marks)

b) Find the probability of...

i) a score of 4 _____ ii) a score of 9 _____ iii) a score of 1 _____ (3 marks)

2 For lunch, Charlotte has a sandwich and a drink. For her sandwich she can choose ham or cheese or beef. For her drink she can choose orange juice or tea. List all the possible lunches that Charlotte can have.

_____

(2 marks)

Score   / 7

GCSE-style questions

Answer all parts of the questions. Show your workings (on a separate sheet of paper if necessary) and include the correct units in your answers.

1 Two fair dice are thrown together and their scores are added.

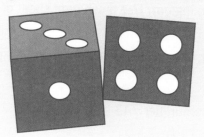

    a) Work out the probability of a score of 7. .... (2 marks)

    b) Work out the probability of a score of 9. .... (2 marks)

2 A youth club has 75 members. The table shows some information about the members.

	Under 13 years old	13 years and over	Total
Boys	15	....	42
Girls	....	21	....
Total	....	....	75

    a) Complete the table. (3 marks)

    b) One of the club members is picked at random. Write down the probability that this member is under 13 years old.

    .... (1 mark)

3 Some students are given a choice of activities. In the morning they can do swimming (S), tennis (T) or art (A), and in the afternoon they have a choice of football (F) or swimming. Write down all the possible combinations that the students can choose if they do one activity in the morning and one activity in the afternoon.

....

.... (2 marks)

4 A company makes a digital component for televisions. The probability that the company makes a faulty digital component is 0.02. The company makes 500 digital components in one hour. The cost of each digital component is £2.50. Work out an estimate of the cost to the company of making faulty digital components per hour. ▦

....

.... (3 marks)

Score   / 13

Statistics and probability

How well did you do?

| 0–6 | Try again | 7–12 | Getting there | 13–19 | Good work | 20–24 | Excellent! |

For more information on this topic, see pages 90–91 of your Success Revision Guide.

85

Mixed GCSE-style questions

Answer these questions. Show full working out. Use a separate sheet of paper if necessary.

1 a) Write the number sixteen thousand, four hundred and sixty-two in figures.

.... **(1 mark)**

b) Write down the value of the 3 in the number 743 271.

.... **(1 mark)**

c) Write the number 7942 rounded to the nearest ten.

.... **(1 mark)**

2 Audrey wishes to make a patio in her garden. The patio must be rectangular and have an area of 12m².

a) On the grid opposite, sketch three different patios for Audrey. Scale: 1 grid square represents 1m.

(3 marks)

b) Audrey decides to have a patio with the largest perimeter. Which patio will Audrey choose? Draw the patio on the grid opposite.

(3 marks)

3 The table below shows the cost of a double room at a hotel.

Day	Cost per person per night	
	Friday to Sunday	Monday to Thursday
Low season	£40.00	£52.00
High season	£45.00	£60.00
Peak season	£60.00	£75.00

Breakfast at the hotel costs £10.50 per person. Mr and Mrs Price stay in a double room for two nights in peak season. They arrive on Sunday and leave on Tuesday morning. They eat breakfast on Monday morning only. How much does it cost Mr and Mrs Price to stay at the hotel?

....

.... **(4 marks)**

4 Comics cost £2.10 each. Calvin buys four comics. He pays with a £20 note. How much change will he get?

.... **(3 marks)**

5 a) Complete the table by writing a sensible metric unit on each dotted line. The first one has been done for you.

The distance from Manchester to London	226 kilometres
The volume of tea in a mug	305 ....
The weight of a £1 coin	11 ....
The height of a room	325 ....

(3 marks)

b) Change 6300 grams into kilograms.

.... kg **(1 mark)**

c) Change 5 inches into centimetres.

.... cm **(1 mark)**

6 Here is a list of eight numbers: 2, 7, 15, 18, 27, 39, 45, 46

a) Write down two numbers from the list with a sum of 63.

.... **(1 mark)**

b) Write down a number from the list that is a factor of 21.

.... **(1 mark)**

c) Write down a number from the list that is a cube number.

.... **(1 mark)**

d) Write down a number from the list that is a multiple of 5.

.... **(1 mark)**

7 On the grid, enlarge the shape with a scale factor of 2.

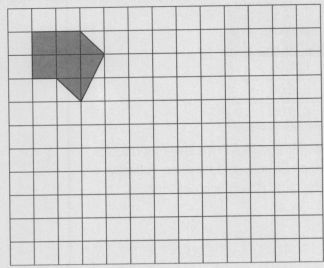

(2 marks)

8 a) Simplify $3a + 5b + 2a - 4b$

_____

(2 marks)

b) Simplify $7x - 2y + 3x - 5y$

_____

(2 marks)

c) Simplify $5a^2 - 3a^2$

_____

(1 mark)

9 In the diagram, WXY is a straight line.

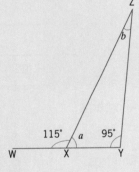

a) i) Work out the size of the angle marked a.

_____ °

(1 mark)

ii) Give a reason for your answer.

_____

(1 mark)

b) i) Work out the size of the angle marked b.

_____ °

(1 mark)

ii) Give a reason for your answer.

_____

(1 mark)

10 A game of darts can be won, drawn or lost. Ahmed plays a game of darts with his friend.

The probability that Ahmed wins the game is 0.25

The probability that Ahmed draws the game is 0.35

a) Work out the probability that Ahmed loses the game of darts.

_____

(2 marks)

b) Work out the probability that Ahmed wins 2 successive games of darts.

_____

(3 marks)

11 The diagram shows the plan of a garden. All the angles are right angles. Tracy wants to turf the garden. Turf costs £3.80 per square metre. You can only buy a whole number of square metres. Standard delivery cost is £17.50. How much will Tracy's turf cost, including delivery?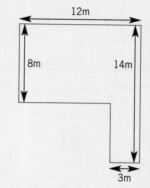

_____

_____

_____

(5 marks)

12 The table gives information about the brands of television available in a shop.

Brand of television	Number in stock
Sharp	6
Panasonic	10
Toshiba	2

Draw an accurate pie chart to show this information.

(3 marks)

13 Katy sells CDs. She sells each CD for £9.20, plus VAT at 17.5%. She sells 127 CDs. Work out how much money Katy receives.

£ _____

(4 marks)

14 Here is a diagram showing the side views of a model. The cubes are either blue or white.

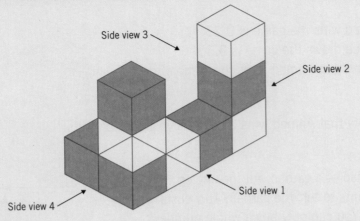

Side view 3

Side view 2

Side view 1

Side view 4

These drawings show the side views of the model. Write down which side view each drawing represents.

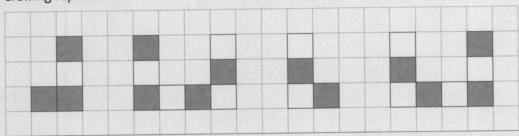

a) Side view _____ **b)** Side view _____ **c)** Side view _____ **d)** Side view _____

(2 marks)

15 Complete this bill. 🖩

Dreams Carpet Cleaners			
Number of rooms/stairs		Cost per room/stair	Total
Living rooms	2	£32.50	
Hall	1	£15.70	£15.70
Stairs	13	£0.60	
Bedrooms	4		£65.00
		Total	
		VAT at 17.5% of total	
		Total amount payable	

(6 marks)

16 The bar chart shows the number of different-coloured cars in a car park.

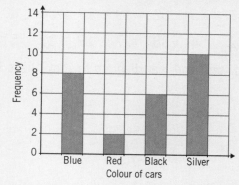

Leo started to draw a pictogram to show the same information. He has shown the number of blue cars. Complete the pictogram.

Blue	● ●
Red	
Black	
Silver	

(3 marks)

17 Here are the first four terms of an arithmetic sequence: 5, 9, 13, 17, ...
Find an expression, in terms of n, for the nth term of the sequence.

_____

(2 marks)

18 Draw the graph of $y = 2x - 1$ on the grid below.

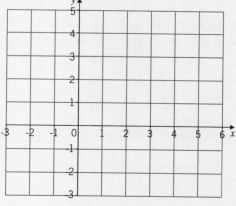

(3 marks)

19 The diagram shows the positions of three towns, A, B and C. Town C is due east of towns A and B. Town B is due east of A.

Town B is $3\frac{1}{3}$ miles from town A. Town C is $1\frac{1}{4}$ miles from town B.
Calculate the number of miles between town A and town C.

_____ miles   (3 marks)

20 Here are the ages in years of the members of a golf club.

9	42	37	28	36	44	47	43	62	19	17	36	40
56	58	32	18	41	52	42	54	38	27	29	32	51

In the space provided, draw an ordered stem-and-leaf diagram to show these ages.

(3 marks)

21 Poppy bought a bumper pack of 12 packets of crisps for £1.44. She sold 11 packets to her friends for 22p each and ate one packet herself. How much profit did Poppy make? 🖩

£ _____

(3 marks)

22 $2.4 \times 320 = 768$

Use this result to write down the answers to the following:

a) 2.4×32 _____ (1 mark)

b) 2.4×3.2 _____ (1 mark)

c) 0.24×0.32 _____ (1 mark)

23 Solve the following:

a) $5n + 2 = 12$ $\qquad n =$ _____ (2 marks)

b) $4a + 3 = 2a + 8$ $\qquad a =$ _____ (2 marks)

c) $5x - 2 = 3(x + 6)$ $\qquad x =$ _____ (2 marks)

d) $\frac{3 - 2x}{4} = 2$ $\qquad x =$ _____ (2 marks)

24 Simplify the following:

a) $p^4 \times p^6$ _____ (1 mark)

b) $\frac{p^7}{p^3}$ _____ (1 mark)

c) $\frac{p^4 \times p^5}{p}$ _____ (1 mark)

25 Megan bought a TV for £700. Each year, the TV depreciated in value by 20%.
Work out the value of the TV one year after she bought it. 🖩

£ ....

26 The table gives the times, to the nearest minute, taken to complete a puzzle.

Time t (nearest minute)	Frequency
$0 \leqslant t < 10$	5
$10 \leqslant t < 20$	12
$20 \leqslant t < 30$	8
$30 \leqslant t < 40$	5

Calculate an estimate for the mean number of minutes taken to complete the puzzle. 🖩

Mean = ... minutes

(4 marks)

27 The diagram shows a triangle ABC.
AB = 6.2cm, BC = 4.9cm
Work out the length x of the side AC.
Give your answer to 1 decimal place. 🖩

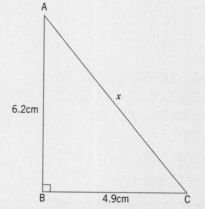

....

.... cm

(3 marks)

28 Isabelle says that when throwing two fair dice, the probability of scoring a double three is greater than the probability of scoring a double one. Is this true? Justify your answer.

....

....

(2 marks)

1 a) 16 462   **b)** 3 thousands   **c)** 7940

2 a)

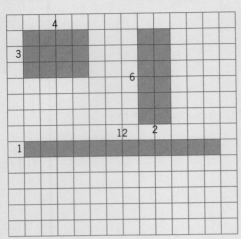

b)

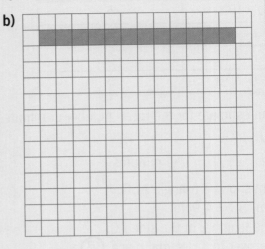

3 Sunday night: 2 × £60.00 = £120.00
Monday night: 2 × £75.00 = £150.00
Breakfast: 2 × £10.50 = £21.00
Total cost = £291

4 4 × £2.10 = £8.40
£20 − £8.40 = £11.60

5 a)

The distance from Manchester to London	226 kilometres
The volume of tea in a mug	305 millilitres
The weight of a £1 coin	11 grams
The height of a room	325 centimetres

b) 6.3kg   **c)** 12.5cm

6 a) 45 and 18   **b)** 7   **c)** 27   **d)** 15 or 45

7

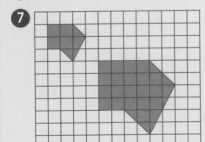

8 a) $5a + b$ **b)** $10x - 7y$ **c)** $2a^2$

9 a) i) 65°   **ii)** Angles on a straight line add up to 180°.

b) i) 20°   **ii)** Angles in a triangle add up to 180° (95° + 65° + 20° = 180°).

10 a) 1 − (0.25 + 0.35)
  = 1 − 0.6
  = 0.4

b) 0.0625 or $\frac{1}{16}$

11 Area of garden: 12 × 8 = 96m², 6 × 3 = 18m², so total = 114m²
114 × £3.80 = £433.20
Delivery = £17.50
Total cost = £433.20 + £17.50 = £450.70

12

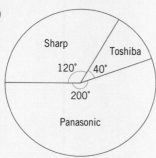

13 9.20 × 1.175 = £10.81 with VAT for each CD
127 × £10.81 = £1372.87

14 a) Side view 4   **b)** Side view 1   **c)** Side view 2   **d)** Side view 3

15

Dreams Carpet Cleaners			
Number of rooms/stairs		**Cost per room/stair**	**Total**
Living rooms	2	£32.50	**£65.00**
Hall	1	£15.70	£15.70
Stairs	13	£0.60	**£7.80**
Bedrooms	4	**£16.25**	£65.00
		Total	**£153.50**
		VAT at 17.5% of total	**£26.86**
		Total amount payable	**£180.36**

16

Blue	●●
Red	◖
Black	●◖
Silver	●●◖

Key: ● = 4 cars

17 4n + 1

18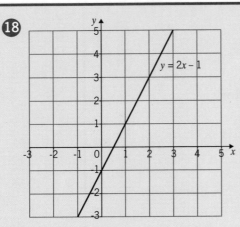

19 $4\frac{7}{12}$ miles

20
```
0 | 9
1 | 7 8 9
2 | 7 8 9
3 | 2 2 6 6 7 8
4 | 0 1 2 2 3 4 7
5 | 1 2 4 6 8
6 | 2
```
Key: 1 | 7 = 17 years

21 $11 \times 22p = £2.42$
Profit = £2.42 – £1.44 = £0.98

22 a) 76.8   **b)** 7.68   **c)** 0.0768

23 a) $5n + 2 = 12$
$5n = 12 - 2$
$5n = 10$
$n = 2$

b) $4a + 3 = 2a + 8$
$2a = 5$
$a = 2.5$

c) $x = 10$

d) $x = -2.5$

24 a) p^{10} **b)** p^4 **c)** p^8

25 £560

26 $19.\dot{3}$ minutes

27 $x^2 = 6.2^2 + 4.9^2$
$x^2 = 38.44 + 24.01$
$x^2 = 62.45$
$x = \sqrt{62.45}$
$x = 7.9$cm

28 The probability of scoring a double three is the same as scoring a double one, since the probability of getting a three or a one when a fair dice is thrown are the same.